A THURINGIAN GLASSHOUSE

THE
Tools of the
Chemist

Their Ancestry and American Evolution

BY

ERNEST CHILD

▼

REINHOLD PUBLISHING CORPORATION

330 WEST FORTY-SECOND STREET, NEW YORK, U. S. A.

1940

Copyright, 1940, by
REINHOLD PUBLISHING CORPORATION

———

~~t#89~~

Printed in the United States of America

BY THE HADDON CRAFTSMEN, INC., CAMDEN, N. J.

PREFACE

I N ONE of his delightful writings about early American
chemical education which have so enriched chemical mem-
orabilia, C. A. Browne, Bureau of Chemistry and Soils, United
States Department of Agriculture, Washington, D. C., said
that the story of laboratory apparatus development deserved
to be written as a part of the history of chemical education
in America.

Some readers may consider it presumptuous, although I
hope not, for an English-born American business man to ac-
cept that challenge. Shortly after I came to this country in
1906, having served a four-year apprenticeship in the scientific apparatus trade in London, England, I became associated
with Eimer & Amend of New York, with whom I remained
for almost ten years. I little realized then that the period was
the dawn of the great modern development in American chemistry and laboratories, and that in no country was there a
greater appreciation of the value of chemical research for the
advancement of chemical knowledge and the development of
the chemical industry. During that period, I was afforded opportunity to visit many of the leading educational and industrial laboratories throughout the country, which provided me
the great good fortune to meet many American chemists and
industrialists who were then, or later became, leaders in chemical education and industry.

My effort primarily concerns the events and those whose
work played a significant part in the creation and development of chemical laboratories and apparatus in America,
rather than evaluation of the scientific achievements of the

3

many who have done so much to stimulate interest in chemistry and for the advancement of science.

A study of the development of chemical apparatus in the United States must necessarily include a survey of the European environment from which it stemmed, and reference to those scientists who originated, designed and made the apparatus they used, not only for themselves but for their contemporaries. The advance and results of science in America have been so far-reaching that, before entering on the story of chemical apparatus, it may not be amiss to review briefly the evolution and development of chemistry in America from its infancy.

My thanks for assistance and encouragement in this work are due many friends, both here and abroad, in particular to C. A. Browne, A. Barclay, Science Museum, South Kensington, London, my old school friend, H. J. Hornby of A. Gallenkamp & Co., Ltd., London and Charles Mohr of Prolabo-Poulenc, Paris, great-grandson of the famous German pharmacist-chemist and apparatus designer, Carl Friedrich Mohr. Grateful acknowledgment is also made to the writings of Edgar F. Smith and to the Chemists' Club of New York for the facilities of their library.

As Kipling said, "Every man must be his own law in his own work, but it is a poor spirited artist in any craft who does not know how the other man's work should be done or improved."

ERNEST CHILD

Garden City,
Long Island, N. Y.
November 22, 1939.

FOREWORD

IN A footnote to the reproduction of an old woodcut of about 1846, showing the apparatus store of Benjamin Pike, Jr., at 294 Broadway, New York, the writer of this foreword in 1932 published the following remark:

"Pike furnished many colleges of this period with apparatus. The supply houses of Chamberlain and of Wightman in Boston also sold chemicals and apparatus to colleges. It was only after 1830 that domestic dealers of chemicals and apparatus began to come into prominence. The story of this development deserves to be written up as a part of the history of chemical education in America."

When this out-of-the-way footnote was published, the writer little supposed that he was casting his bread upon the waters. He had tried in vain to learn something about the early manufacturers and sellers of chemical apparatus; and, finally realizing that this special branch of historical chemistry must be investigated by one who has had years of contact with the scientific instrument business, he dismissed the subject from his mind. Great was his surprise and pleasure, therefore, a few years later, when Mr. Ernest Child, long associated with manufacturers and dealers in chemical equipment in America and Europe, announced to him that he accepted the challenge and was preparing to write a book upon the subject.

After several years of most painstaking research at home and abroad, Mr. Child has condensed the results of his labors in the present volume entitled "The Tools of the Chemist— their Ancestry and American Evolution." It has been the privilege of the writer to glance over the manuscript of this work

5

before its publication; and after reviewing it he can only say
that the questions which he had asked in vain about manufacturers and sellers of chemical apparatus seven years ago have
now been fully answered. It is a work which could be written only by one who has the double endowment of the patience that belongs to the historical investigator and of the
knowledge that has come from long association with the scientific apparatus business.

The history of apparatus and of its role in science and industry has never been sufficiently appreciated either by the
specialist or by the public at large. But a changing attitude in
this respect is now becoming apparent. This is well indicated
by the recent election of a manufacturer of scientific instruments, Mr. Robert S. Whipple, to the Presidency of Section
A (on Mathematical and Physical Sciences) of the British Association for the Advancement of Science. His presidential address on "Instruments in Science and Industry"* gives a most
illuminating account of the importance which instruments
have played in the historical advancement of science. The
present work of Mr. Child is a further evidence of the growing appreciation of apparatus as a factor in the development
of science and industry. We learn from its pages how distinguished scientists themselves, like Gay-Lussac, were led
from being inventors of apparatus to become commercial
manufacturers of scientific equipment.

The old attitude which regards the sellers of scientific apparatus as mercenary and tainted with commercialism has for
the most part disappeared. Accum, who discharged the double
vocation of scientist and tradesman in London a century and
a quarter ago, was one of the earliest to refute this charge. "I
would submit," he declared, "that he who establishes a place
of fabrication, or deposit, of an article of use to the sciences,

---

* *Nature*, pp. 461-5, September 9, 1939.

which could not before be purchased, is a benefactor to the public."

The readers of Part III on "Distributors of Chemical Laboratory Apparatus" will be convinced of the truth of this statement. Chemists, manufacturers and all others who handle chemical equipment are especially indebted to Mr. Child for the information which he has gathered for the first time on the history of the dealers in chemical equipment in the different cities of the United States. The writer of this foreword will venture the guess that the preparation of this concluding part of the book, although comprising but a fifth of the total work, involved more labor and correspondence than was encountered in writing all the preceding sections.

In the historical development of his subject, Mr. Child has very properly gone back to European origins. From the time of John Winthrop the Younger, in 1633, until the outbreak of the World War in 1914, American chemists were dependent upon European manufacturers and dealers for most of their scientific equipment. These importations, as Mr. Child points out, were stimulated by the return from their laboratory studies in European universities of hundreds of American students who, becoming the future leaders in chemical education and industry in America, naturally employed the apparatus with which they were most familiar. This movement, which began in the early eighteen hundreds, continued with increasing acceleration until after the close of the nineteenth century.

But the forces that were to make American chemists independent of foreign manufacturers and sellers of apparatus were simultaneously gathering headway. This was largely brought about by the emigration of skilled mechanicians from Europe to the United States—such men as Pike from England, Becker from Holland, Quettier from France, and the host of glass-blowers and instrument-makers who came

from Germany as a result of the political disturbances of
1848-49. These men set up establishments for the manufacture and sale of domestic scientific apparatus, and the apprentices whom they trained became in turn the proprietors of
other factories and emporiums. The foundations were thus
laid for the manufacture of scientific apparatus in the United
States on an independent scale, and the outbreak of the World
War was the event that brought the movement to its final successful culmination.

Mr. Child, in opening up the new field of research so en-
tertainingly described in the present volume, would be the
last to suppose that his work is complete. He has very successfully assembled many of the pieces of a complicated pic-
ture puzzle, but other pieces are lacking. A history of this
kind should have been written a half century or more ago
when the men were alive who could supply information that
is at present lacking. It is hoped that scientists whose mem-
ories and traditions go back several generations may help Mr.
Child to supply some of these missing details. We would like
to know more about Jacob Perkins of Newburyport, the inventor of the piezometer and other scientific instruments, and
about Joseph Zentmayer, the German refugee and inventor of
scientific apparatus, whose shop in Philadelphia for the manufacture of microscopes, lenses and other equipment was a fa-
vorite rendezvous for scientists seventy years ago. Many a
scientist has received inspiration from the random talk with
colleagues and mechanics in shops like those of Zentmayer.
The social debt which science owes the instrument maker
and dealer has been almost forgotten.

It is hoped that this instructive account will stimulate
others to investigate further this interesting and long-neglected
subject.

C. A. BROWNE

TABLE OF CONTENTS

LIST OF ILLUSTRATIONS

PART I

PART II

Part I

PEOPLE and EVENTS

in

AMERICAN CHEMISTRY

CHEMICAL HOUSE OF LIBAVIUS

*Take interest, I implore you, in those sacred dwellings which
one designates by the expressive term:* LABORATORIES.
*Demand that they be multiplied, that they be adorned;
These are the temples of the future—temples of well being
and happiness;
There it is that humanity grows greater, stronger, better.*

LOUIS PASTEUR.

ONE of the earliest literary references to the laboratory
was made by the German chemist Libavius (1540-
1616) in his celebrated "Alchymia," first published in 1595.
His ideal "chemical house" or laboratory was one of the first
planned on lines opposed to the alchemical laboratories. In his
text-book he delineates it both in plan and elevation. Besides
the main laboratory, it contained a store-room for chemicals,
a preparation room and several other rooms providing every
facility for experimentation. Not least among the amenities
was a wine cellar, a delightful feature (says Holmyard*) un-
happily overlooked by the modern architect of chemical laboratories.

The first laboratory within what is now the United States
was established in 1631 by John Winthrop (1606-1676),
one of the founders of the Royal Society of London and son
of the Puritan leader who became the first Governor of the
Massachusetts Colony. Winthrop was possessed of a vigorous
mind which led him to a most eventful life and to be the
pioneer spirit of our early crude chemical industries. He furnished Geo. Starkey (Harvard, 1646) with chemical books,
chemicals and glasses (the general term used in the seven-

* Eric John Holmyard, "Makers of Chemistry," Oxford, Clarendon Press,
1931.

ALCHEMIST'S LABORATORY

From an exhibit in the Deutsches Museum, Munich

teenth century for chemical glassware), alembics, etc. An old London letter said of Starkey* "His extraordinary knowledge of chemistry led him to discover an effectual cure of the plague"; nevertheless, he is said to have died in London of the plague.

The meager science equipment of Harvard College was greatly extended by the apparatus donated in 1728 by Thomas Hollis (1659-1711). A merchant of London, he founded in 1726 the Chair of Mathematics and Natural History, and was one of the early promoters of scientific study in America. His purpose in donating the apparatus—"the advancement of natural and revealed religion"—gives some idea of the scientific notions of those days. This apparatus and other valued treasures were housed in Harvard Hall, an ancient building, which was destroyed by fire on the tempestuous winter night of January 24, 1764.

Little is recorded of the laboratory of Winthrop and other early American chemists, but we may be sure they were not patterned on the sumptuous lines of Libavius' "ideal house," as for a long time the idea persisted that a basement which usually provided dismal surroundings was the only fit place for a laboratory. What a feast the early pioneers would enjoy could they but see the modern temples of laboratories, many so richly endowed by the benevolence of those who profited from the chemical achievements built on the work of our early chemists!

For many years, Astronomy, Mineralogy, Pharmacy, Medicine and Geology were the sciences of interest. Little was done in this country toward the theoretical side of chemistry although much had been accomplished on the practical side. Demonstration lectures, which gave impetus to the diffusion of scientific knowledge among the people, were the method of teaching chemistry until the early decades of the nineteenth

* Massachusetts Historical Society.

century. Our medical colleges early recognized chemistry as a branch of medical study and at the close of the eighteenth century, four such institutions offered instruction in the fore-mentioned sciences and chemistry. The College of New Jersey (since 1896 known as Princeton University) was the only seminary of learning other than the medical schools to teach chemistry from a separate chair.

Courtesy of the Edgar Fahs Smith Memorial Collection, University of Pennsylvania

BENJAMIN RUSH

A few years after graduating from Princeton in 1760, Benjamin Rush, a signatory of the Declaration of Independence, who later studied abroad under Joseph Black in Edinburgh and other teachers, began to practise medicine in Philadelphia. At the same time he gave scientific lectures at the Philadelphia Medical College—later absorbed by the University of Pennsylvania. Although Rush owes his well-earned repu-

tation to labors in other sciences, he was the first to hold an
independent Chair of Chemistry in this country. To him is
attributed the laying of the foundation stone of chemical education in our country, although, according to C. A. Browne,*
there is evidence that James Smith in 1767 was appointed to
teach chemistry at Kings College (now Columbia University),
New York.

Rush was succeeded by James Woodhouse, a graduate of
the University's Medical School. In 1797 he issued his book,
"The Young Chemists' Pocket Companion," which gave pictures of apparatus in use at that time, including a set which
he called "a portable laboratory."

Joseph Priestley (1733-1804), the English chemist and Non-
conformist minister, discoverer of oxygen, openly expressed
his sympathy with the French Revolutionists, which aroused
great feeling against him in England and he decided it wise
in 1794 to emigrate to America. Priestley made his first head-
quarters in Philadelphia and became closely associated with
the students and teachers at the University of Pennsylvania.
At his death in Northumberland, Pennsylvania, in 1804, he
undoubtedly possessed the best-equipped scientific laboratory
in this country. Much of his apparatus, which was imported
from England, is preserved in the Joseph Priestley Museum at
Northumberland.

John Maclean (1771-1814), born in Glasgow, Scotland,
came to this country in 1795 and in that year was appointed
the first Professor of Chemistry at Princeton. His guardian
was the father of Charles Macintosh (1766-1843), the inventor of waterproof fabrics and an early associate of Thomas
Hancock, of whom we shall speak later in connection with
laboratory rubber ware. The limitation of apparatus at this
period is strikingly indicated in Maclean's† letter of August

* Our Chemical Heritage, *Ind. Eng. Chem.,* **27**, 501 (1935).
† "Lectures on Combustion," Princeton University Press, William Foster,
1929.

PRIESTLEY'S OXYGEN APPARATUS AND BURNING GLASS

1803, to Benjamin Silliman at Yale College, who regarded Maclean as his earliest master in chemistry.

"On looking over the list of articles of chemical apparatus in your possession they appear to be sufficient for teaching the principles of chemistry. Perhaps a mercurial pneumatic-chemical trough, a galvanic apparatus, a large double convex lens, and a simple apparatus for the decomposition of water might be added to it with advantage. But there is no end to chemical apparatus. An experimenter will every now and then find that he is in want of something which it was impossible to foresee. However, this is a principle which ought never to be lost sight of, that the more simple an apparatus (provided it be sufficient), the better. A complicated set of machinery, without adding to the accuracy of the experiments, tends to bewilder the student; while a man with plenty of bottles, tubes and corks may, with the assistance of a blowpipe, vary his apparatus so as to perform an infinity of experiments as well for use as amusement."

This letter from Maclean to Silliman reflects a philosophy expressed in the eighth century by Jabir ibn Hayyan, the great chemist of Islam, who is recorded to have said:

"The first essential in chemistry is that thou shouldst perform practical work and conduct experiments, for he who performs not practical work nor makes experiments will never attain to the least degree of mastery. But thou, Oh my son, do thou experiment so that thou mayest acquire knowledge. Scientists delight not in abundance of material; they rejoice only in the excellence of their experimental methods."

Courtesy Director of the Science Museum, London

APPARATUS USED BY PRIESTLEY IN HIS EXPERIMENTS ON GASES

*Courtesy of the Edgar Fahs Smith Memorial
Collection, University of Pennsylvania*

ROBERT HARE

A great teacher, an entertaining lecturer, and an inventor
and maker of much apparatus for demonstration and investi-
gational work, Robert Hare (1781-1858) was appointed in
1818 to the Chair of Chemistry in the Medical Department
of the University of Pennsylvania. The fertility of his inven-
tive mind is illustrated by numerous and ingenious forms of
apparatus which he devised, including a compound oxy-hydrogen blowpipe which made possible the first commercial smelting of platinum, a calorimotor and deflagrator, a source of
electric energy. Hare was greatly interested in "pneumatic
chemistry," the art of collecting, measuring and distinguishing
gaseous substances, and he devised several forms of pneumatic
troughs and other apparatus for this purpose. J. B. Van Hel-
mont (1577-1644), a Belgian chemist, who gave us the word
gas (from "chaos"), was the founder of this art. He was the
first to understand that there are gases distinct from atmospheric air, although he did not succeed in collecting them. A
century later, the art was greatly extended by Priestley, who
was the first to use mercury in place of water, which made
possible the collection of gases soluble in water. Before the
days of piped running water, Hare devised the type of trough
illustrated. It included a cask for water storage with devices
to pump and keep the water at the required level. "Das Laboratorium," published in Weimar, which illustrates the standard
apparatus of the period 1825-1840, includes several pictures
of Hare's apparatus. Hare furnished duplicates of his apparatus
to Faraday. A great loss to the limited collection of early
American apparatus was sustained when Hare's apparatus, as
well as the burning glass used by Priestley in his experiments,
was destroyed by the fire which occurred at the Smithsonian
Institution, Washington, D. C., in 1864.

The teachings for over sixty years of Benjamin Silliman
(1779-1864) brought about in this country an awakening to
the value of a knowledge of the natural sciences, and led many

APPARATUS FROM HARE'S COMPENDIUM, 1828

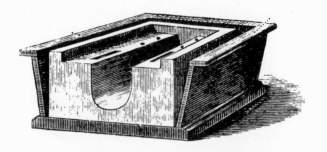

HARE'S MERCURIAL PNEUMATIC CISTERN

The cistern was of solid marble, enclosed in a wooden box, arranged to catch any metal spilling over the cistern. To fill completely required almost 600 pounds of mercury

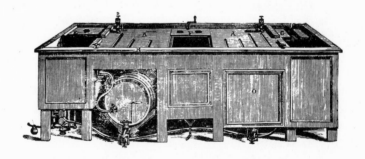

HARE'S HYDRO-PNEUMATIC CISTERN

Used in the days before piped running water

HARE'S COMPOUND BLOWPIPE

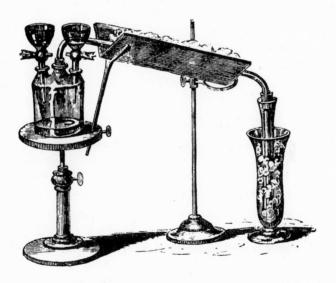

APPARATUS FOR PREPARING NITROUS ETHER
The condensing arrangement seems to be
the progenitor of Liebig's condenser

Courtesy C. A. Browne

BENJAMIN SILLIMAN

academic schools to provide for the study of chemistry, but not laboratory work, which was almost unknown at this period. Silliman studied under Woodhouse, but according to Edgar F. Smith, he found the greatest stimulus in his fellow pupil Hare. He later received instruction under Accum in London, of whom we shall speak again. Although not a great original investigator, Silliman was a master executive, a prolific writer, and a popular scientific lecturer who caused many a young man to become interested in chemistry. The fact that he had studied law and had been admitted to the bar before he took up chemistry probably contributed to his skill as a lecturer. In 1804, Silliman started his teaching career at Yale College as Professor of Chemistry, Pharmacy, Mineralogy and Geology, in a gloomy underground room where he worked for many years. Among his many listeners who contributed to the development of scientific education in America were Amos Eaton and Josiah P. Cooke, who came to occupy for over forty years the Chair of Chemistry at Harvard College.

Amos Eaton (1776-1842) at Rensselaer School, Troy, New York—the first school to be established in the United States primarily for the teaching of science and engineering, and for many years a mecca for teachers of applied science—was a teacher possessed of unusual ability to imbue his pupils with a love for research. After studying under Silliman at Yale, Eaton commenced in 1824 to deliver a series of lectures along the route of the Erie Canal. The versatility of the scientific pursuits of the early teachers in America and an indication that many unqualified lecturers were taking advantage of the growing interest in science, is revealed in the first chapter of his book, "Chemical Instructor," which gives also a list of the required apparatus and chemicals.

"In commencing an itinerating course, let the Clergymen, Doctors, Lawyers, and other principal men in the village or district, send printed cards (prepared by the lecturer) inviting the citizens to attend a gratuitous lecture.

"At the first lecture, in all cases (even in colleges), the plan and object of the proposed course should be illustrated by striking experiments. But never introduce those blazing, puppet-show-like experiments, common with quacks and impostors.

"Never offer less than 24 lectures for a course. To save the public from imposition, make the fact known, as extensively as possible, that none but impostors will offer less than 15 lectures for a course; and that 30 ought to be given. These peddling swindlers, who offer to sell tickets for isolated lectures, ought to be despised. They are always contemptible quacks of no integrity; and they ought not be allowed to sleep near traveler's baggage, at public inns.

"Itinerating lectures on Chemistry, Natural Philosophy (including astronomy), Geology and Botany, are of great use to small villages and country districts where permanent courses cannot be supported. Nothing short of full courses, however, should be commenced. From 24 to 30 exercises in Chemistry, the same on Botany, 12 on Geology, 12 on Mathematical Philosophy, 8 on Astronomy, if well conducted, will be useful. But every city, large village or populous district, ought to be too liberal to depend on itinerating lecturers. They should support permanent teachers, of the right kind; particularly avoid those self-styled chemists, who swarm about our large towns, possessing no qualifications but impudence. These are chiefly foreigners; and most of them are illiterate Scotch, Irish or English. But justice demands, that we make many honorable exceptions."

JOSEPH BLACK

OVER the formative period in America which we have
briefly reviewed, when chemistry had hardly attained
the rank of a science and journals and periodicals devoted to
science were few, our teachers and experimenters avidly followed the publications of the various learned societies of Europe. They read the writings of the Scotch, French and English scientists who were shedding a flood of light on the new
chemical philosophy of the period. In 1818 Silliman of Yale
started his journal which gave notes of his experiments and
abstracts of the work and discoveries in science, both here
and abroad. The apparatus used by these early scientists usually was described in much detail in their writing, and was
accompanied by accurate drawings to enable the reader to
duplicate the apparatus for his own experimentation.

HENRY CAVENDISH

Among the European pioneers in science whose experiments and writings were a powerful influence on early scientific thought in America were: Joseph Black (1728-1799), a Scotch chemist, whose researches formed the beginnings of quantitative chemistry and who was the first to use the balance in chemical research; Henry Cavendish (1731-1810), who devised much apparatus, including the famous Eudiom-

ANTOINE LAURENT LAVOISIER

eter used for some of his classic experiments during which he discovered the composition of water; Antoine Laurent Lavoisier (1743-1794), the great exponent of quantitative analysis who stormed the last defenses of the phlogistonists and gave the name *oxygen* to Priestley's gas, later to meet his death on the guillotine during the French Revolution; Karl Wilhelm Scheele (1742-1786), a poor Swedish apothecary, discoverer of many chemical facts of great importance; Gay-Lussac (1778-1850), the eminent French scientist, noted for his law of the expansion of gases, who devised much apparatus, including his famous burette and vapor density apparatus; Dumas (1800-1884), French chemist, renowned for his methods for ascertaining vapor densities; a prolific writer on applied

FARADAY IN HIS LABORATORY AT THE ROYAL INSTITUTION, LONDON

Courtesy Journal of Chemical Education

MICHAEL FARADAY

chemistry who was one of the first men in France to realize the importance of laboratory training. John Dalton (1766-1844), noted for his atomic theory which was for many years the foundation of modern chemistry; Sir Humphry Davy (1778-1829), brilliant lecturer at the Royal Institution, London; Michael Faraday (1791-1867), father of electrochemistry and discoverer of benzene, whose services in connection with scientific problems, were in much demand by commercially minded people before his real scientific abilities were fully realized; and Jöns Jacob Berzelius (1779-1848), the great Swedish scientist, who effected many improvements in analytical methods and the technique of the blowpipe, and who was the teacher of the famous Wöhler.

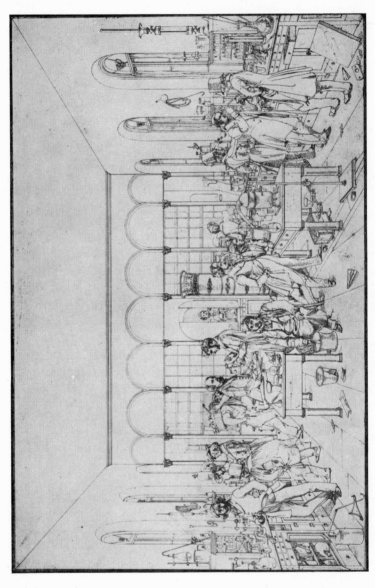

STUDENTS IN LIEBIG'S LABORATORY, 1842

Every theory which urges men to labor and research, which excites acuteness and sustains perseverance, is a gain to science, for it is labor and research which lead to discoveries.

LIEBIG.

THE early years of the nineteenth century witnessed a marked extension of chemical knowledge in Europe, which created a desire for more practical knowledge. This led the Scotch chemist, Thomas Thomson (1773-1852) to establish in Glasgow the first chemical laboratory to offer students facilities for practical work; however, systematic instruction with laboratory facilities for students was inaugurated by the famed German chemist, Justus von Liebig (1803-1873). After obtaining his doctorate and working in the private laboratory of Gay-Lussac and other French scientists, Liebig was appointed Professor of Chemistry at Giessen. His writings and gifts as a teacher, together with the laboratory training given by Wöhler, not only gave a great impetus to the progress of chemical education in Germany, but attracted students from all over the world, those returning to America infusing new activity and accuracy into our chemical education.

This German influence on chemistry gave rise to a constant flow of new apparatus which the German manufacturers quickly made available to the world; and by the time the development of laboratory instruction in America was under way, the necessity for the experimenter or student to make his own apparatus had materially lessened. Laboratory apparatus catalogs from 1848 onward reflect the great advance and the many modifications and improvements of the original apparatus which have been made during the march of chemical

BÜFF, WÖHLER, KOPP AND LIEBIG (1850)

progress. Liebig, who made his chemical laboratory and course
of instruction the model for all others, was a great contributor
of original chemical apparatus, his potash bulb and condenser*
being best known. A visible proof of America's regard for the
teacher of so many of her distinguished sons is the button of
the American Chemical Society, on which is depicted Liebig's
potash bulb.

* The original metal Liebig condenser is exhibited in the Deutsches Museum, Munich.

The pattern set by Liebig was adopted by Wöhler when he went to Göttingen. Many American students including Booth, Edgar F. Smith, Goessman, Joy, Chandler, Nason, Caldwell and others, who became outstanding teachers in the United States and who in their turn contributed so much to the development of early chemical education in this country, studied under Wöhler.

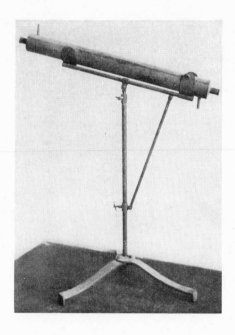

LIEBIG'S ORIGINAL CONDENSER
Deutsches Museum, Munich

A disciple of Liebig, under whom another group to become notable American teachers and chemists studied at Marburg and after 1851 at Heidelberg, was Robert William von Bunsen (1811-1899), who probably is best known for the spectroscope which he devised in 1859 jointly with G. R.

HEMPEL'S ORIGINAL GAS ANALYSIS APPARATUS (1879)
Deutsches Museum, Munich

Kirchhoff. Bunsen spent much of his valuable time designing apparatus, for he realized that successful laboratory results required the proper appliances with which to work. The simple burner which made possible the use of coal gas for heating purposes, a filter pump, an electric battery, an ice calorimeter and a photometer, are among his outstanding apparatus contributions to science.

Among others in the long line of early German scientists to whom acknowledgment is due for contributing apparatus which has continued over the years to be the standard form, or to be modified by others, are Hempel, for his gas analysis apparatus; Hoffmann, for his lecture apparatus in particular; Fresenius, to whom the chemical world is indebted for perfecting and systematizing the various methods of analytical chemistry; Scheibler (1827-1899), a sugar research chemist, for his well-known desiccator; Soxhlet (1848-1905), an agricultural chemist and later Director of the Agricultural Experiment Station at Bavaria, for his widely used extraction apparatus; Erlenmeyer (1825-1905), Professor of Chemistry in Heidelberg, for the form of flask and other apparatus bearing his name; Geissler, the famous German glassblower, of whom we shall again speak, who designed and manufactured much chemical glassware. Mohr (1806-1879), the outstanding scientific pharmacist of his time in Germany, contributed to chemistry the present-day burette which supplanted the Gay-Lussac type long in use, a condenser, clamps, pinchcocks, pipettes and other apparatus, including a specific gravity balance which was the standard form for a long time, until improved by Westphal. Son of a well-to-do druggist in Coblenz and close friend of Liebig, Mohr, because of his poor health, received much of his early education in his father's laboratory. About 1888, a few years after Witt published a description of his perforated filter plate, Ernst Büchner,* German industrial

---

* Fisher, H. L., *Ind. Eng. Chem.* (*News Edition*), 17, 308 (1939).

KJELDAHL AND HIS ORIGINAL APPARATUS FOR NITROGEN DETERMINATION
From a painting in the Carlsberg Laboratory, Copenhagen

CARL FRIEDRICH MOHR

chemist, devised his well-known funnel, the original of which was made of enameled iron.

The Kipp generator, known to every budding chemist before the era of a piped supply of hydrogen sulphide to each laboratory bench, was designed about 1862 by P. J. Kipp (1806-1864), a Dutch chemist. Possessed of considerable scholarship and marked business ability, he founded an apothecary shop in Delft, Holland, in 1830, and soon thereafter started to deal in chemical and physical apparatus. To the Danish scientist Kjeldahl (1849-1900), we are indebted for his widely used* apparatus for nitrogen determination. His original work

* The original apparatus employed a copper Florence form flask. It is not known whether Kjeldahl was the originator of the pear-shaped flask, long used in this determination.

was conducted in 1883 at the Carlsberg Laboratorium, Copenhagen. This research institution, as well as other Danish institutions of Science and Art, was endowed under the Carlsberg Foundation by the founder of the famous Carlsberg Brewery, and supported by the profits of this great brewery which are devoted solely to these purposes.

(*Right*) KIPP'S ORIGINAL GAS GENERATOR

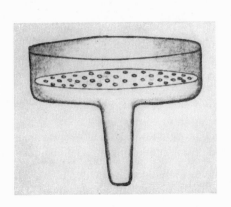

BÜCHNER'S ORIGINAL FUNNEL

With the exception of experimental apparatus designed by a few of our early scientists and improvements to existing apparatus to meet the requirements of new methods, and also of new apparatus for which credit is given in the text, American laboratory workers prior to the World War (1914-1918) had little opportunity to devise apparatus, as the fundamental forms had been introduced long before chemistry made much headway in this country.

E POCHAL developments at Harvard and Yale established
the deep and broad foundation of chemistry in America. One of the first of a long line of American teachers to
study under Liebig, Eben Norton Horsford in 1847 was appointed Rumford Professor at Harvard, and he was almost im-
mediately transferred to teach chemistry in the Lawrence
Scientific School of Harvard University. This school had been
established under an endowment provided by Abbott Lawrence (1792-1855), one of New England's early merchant
princes. The Rumford chair "for the Application of Science
to the useful Arts" was endowed by a native of Massachusetts,
Benjamin Thompson, Count Rumford (1753-1814). In 1859,
Horsford joined in a business partnership for the manufacture
of chemicals. The company was named "Rumford Chemical
Works" after the founder of the chair at Harvard. In the museum of the company at Rumford, Rhode Island, may be seen
many pieces of apparatus used by Horsford, including one of
the first polariscopes used in America. Instruction in chemistry at Harvard began with the founding of the Medical
School in 1782, but laboratory facilities were not provided.
This era ended in 1850 with the appointment of a recent graduate, Josiah Parsons Cooke, to teach chemistry. In the basement of University Hall, he installed the university's first
chemical laboratory. It was provided with neither running
water nor gas. Charles E. Munroe (1849-1938) who probably
witnessed a longer span of chemical progress than any other
American, was an early instructor at the Lawrence Scientific
School. He graduated in 1868 from the Cambridge (Massachusetts) High School, the first secondary school in America
to adopt laboratory instruction. As we have earlier noted, Benjamin Silliman (1779-1864) commenced his teaching career at

YALE ANALYTICAL LABORATORY (1847)

Yale University in 1804, as Professor of Chemistry. Some years later, regular laboratory courses were started by his son. This led to the founding in 1847 of the Yale Analytical Laboratory, which was financially supported by Silliman and Norton until the name of the institution was changed to Sheffield Scientific School, in recognition of the benefactions of Joseph E. Sheffield.

Williams College was one of the first colleges in America to teach chemistry from a separate chair. Ever since the founding of the College in 1793, chemistry was taught, but more as an element of general culture than as a science. The limited laboratory work and the equipment was expanded in 1872, when Ira Remsen (1846-1927) accepted the Chair of Chemistry and Physics. Having secured his Ph.D. in 1870 at Göttingen under Fittig, Remsen had become greatly imbued with the fascination of research. He did not remain long at Williams, accepting in 1876 the Chair of Chemistry at the newly

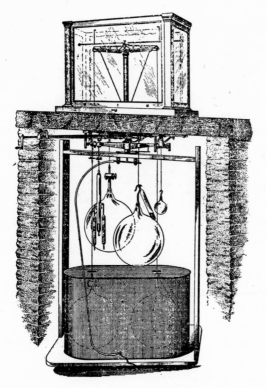

MORLEY'S APPARATUS FOR DETERMINING THE DENSITY OF GASES

founded Johns Hopkins University, the pioneer American graduate school. Williams gave to American chemistry one of its greatest figures, Edward Morley, of the class of 1860. For his original research, Morley (1839-1923) showed great skill in the devising and manipulation of apparatus. Much of the apparatus he used at the Western Reserve University in his classical experiments on the densities of atmospheric gases—mercury still, blast lamp, platinum vessels, etc.—he donated to his alma mater, and personally installed them in the Thompson Chemical Laboratory of Williams College.

Courtesy Journal of Chemical Education

JAMES CURTIS BOOTH

FOR a long time, as the reader has seen, systematic instruction in the theory and practice of chemistry received scant attention by our academic institutions, students being thrown largely on their own resources and expected to perform many of the experiments with apparatus made with their own hands. Prominent among the privately owned laboratories in this country to offer the best means of learning the methods of chemical analysis, were those of Charles Thomas Jackson (1805-1880), of Boston, and James Curtis Booth (1810-1888), of Philadelphia.

Booth, a pupil of Amos Eaton at the Rensselaer School, Troy, New York, in 1830, was one of the first American students to go abroad to extend his knowledge of chemistry under the then growing German influence. After working in Cassel under Wöhler in 1833, Booth returned to Philadelphia and established a student laboratory which came to specialize

The subscriber has taken a Laboratory, in which he proposes to perform analyses of the various ores, as those of iron, lead, copper, silver, gold, &c.; of the earths, as those of lime, clay, sand, &c.; and likewise of the products of art. Instruction in the methods of analysis will also be communicated. The terms will be moderate, and varied in proportion to the difficulty of the performance.

Application for the above purposes may be made to the subscriber in the course of two or three weeks, at his Laboratory, in the old Mint, in Seventh street, between Market and Arch.

Reference may be made to the following gentlemen:—Prof. A. D. BACHE, W. H. KEATING and HENRY TROTH, Esqs.

                                                            JAS. C. BOOTH.
Philadelphia, March 10, 1836.

BOOTH'S FIRST BUSINESS ANNOUNCEMENT

in analytical and consulting work as college facilities grew. For many years, Martin Boyé was associated with him in chemical instruction and lectures. In 1848, Thomas H. Garrett, who had studied in Booth's laboratory, and in 1878, Andrew H. Blair, a graduate of the United States Naval Academy (1866), who had been the chemist for the United States Board for testing metals, joined with Booth, when the firm name was changed to Booth, Garrett and Blair. They were the first consulting chemists to provide America's growing iron and steel industry with real methods of chemical control. Blair was the author of "Chemical Analysis of Iron," which became a standard text-book on the subject; and many pieces of apparatus described in his book, most of which he devised, are still known under his name.

Courtesy Journal of Chemical Education

CHARLES FREDERICK CHANDLER

AN IMMORTAL of American chemistry, Charles Frederick Chandler (1836-1925) was born of fine New England stock at Lancaster, Massachusetts. His life constituted one of the longest chapters in the history of American chemistry and was notable for eminent services in the advancement of chemical education and the fostering and development of chemical laboratories. After formal academic schooling at the Lawrence Scientific School, which he entered in 1853 when sixteen years of age, Chandler studied under Wöhler at Göttingen, where he obtained his doctorate, and under Rose in Berlin. Soon after returning to this country, he was appointed Professor of Chemistry at Union College, Schenectady, and in 1864 he became one of the founders of the School of Mines of Columbia University, when Columbia was a college of the old-fashioned kind. Chandler devised, in 1868, the now universally adopted system of assay ton weights.

An enthusiastic investigator of chemical problems, especially those arising from the application of the science of chemistry to the public health and to many forms of industrial activity, Chandler was above all a great teacher, "a master potter" possessed of a remarkable personality and a profound understanding of the chemical problems of the period and their development. In addition to his manifold activities, he gave a regular course of lectures at the College of Physicians and Surgeons and the New York College of Pharmacy. On his resignation as Professor of Chemistry at Columbia University, the "Columbia Jester" of January 20, 1910, said of him, "Year after year he has taken the entering classes by the hand and led them through the course of Chemistry, Ethics and Humor, so cleverly combined that it has made men of them." At this same time, the unique Chemical Museum at the University built up mainly by Chandler and in no small degree by his generosity, was decreed by the University trustees to be thereafter known as the Chandler Chemical Museum. Chandler's ability as an organizer and leader led to the creation of the American Chemical Society, of which he was an early president, and of the Chemists' Club of New York, whose destiny, as the first president, he guided through its critical early years. In 1909, Morris Loeb, Professor of Chemistry in New York University, was elected president of the club. It was due mainly to his indefatigable efforts and generous financial aid that we have the present Chemists' Club Building at 52 East 41st Street, New York. With its excellent library and congenial atmosphere for meetings and gatherings, the club has become the rendezvous for out-of-town as well as resident chemists.

CHARLES B. DUDLEY

THE effect of the Civil War upon chemical education and industry in America checked the tide of progress for many years. Industry occasionally had casual tests made by consulting chemists, but much skepticism prevailed as to the value of the services of a university trained scientific man; indeed, in the early '80's, in Philadelphia, a cradle of American chemistry, there were less than a dozen industrial chemical laboratories.

The change from the era of rule of thumb control in industry to one of scientific control, can be attributed in large measure to the Pennsylvania Railroad, when they appointed as their chemist C. B. Dudley (1842-1909), born at Oxford, New York, to devote himself exclusively to the commercial and research problems of their organization. A fellow pupil of Chandler under Wöhler, Dudley obtained his degree at the Sheffield Scientific School of Yale University. Shortly after, in 1875, he established at Altoona, Pa., the first railroad laboratory in America, starting the commercial practice of purchasing materials on specifications. This terrorized the steel and many other industries who did not like the idea of scientific dictation. Endowed with keen powers of observation and analysis and supported by the power of the Pennsylvania Railroad, he was able to enforce his demands. Dudley may well be called "Father of the Industrial Control Laboratory." His laboratory, the prototype of many of that class, became a training school for young chemists.

The consternation at this period caused by Dudley's methods, is well illustrated by John K. Winkler, in his book, "Incredible Carnegie."*

"In the early 80's [*sic*] when chemistry was beginning to reform the old hit-or-miss methods in the steel trade, Capt. Bill Jones was profanely alarmed when the Pennsylvania Railroad specified that rails should be of a certain composition. Such curious lingo as 'carbon' and 'manganese' were Greek to him. 'Charlie,' he said to his young assistant Schwab, 'this damned chemistry is going to ruin the steel business.' Charlie soothed the ruffled master and undertook to see that the railroad got the required units of carbon and manganese."

In his autobiography, Andrew Carnegie (1835-1919), who once jokingly suggested his own epitaph, "Here lies one who knew how to get around him men more clever than himself," claims to have employed the first chemist in the iron industry, at his Lucy furnace in 1870. As this furnace did not go into blast until 1872,† Carnegie must have been thinking of the chemist Fricke, whom he brought here from Germany and who quickly proved his value by discovering ore of high iron content in many mines that were thought to be of no value. It is recorded, however, that Robert W. Hunt was chemist in 1860 at the Cambria Iron Works,‡ the cradle of many great

* Garden City Publishing Co., 1931.
† *Iron Age*, 1873.
‡ Stephen L. Goodale, "Chronology of Iron & Steel," 1931.

iron and steel makers, and that Peter Cooper, in 1867, employed a Swedish chemist, Syöberg, to evaluate ores for use at
his Trenton (New Jersey) Iron Works. Hunt, who in 1888
founded under his name the well-known firm of Inspection
and Consulting Engineers, had learned his chemistry in the
laboratory of Booth in Philadelphia. After the Civil War he
was in charge of the experimental Bessemer works at Wyan-
dotte, Michigan, returning to the Cambria works in 1866,
where under his supervision in 1867, the first steel rails were
rolled in this country. In 1912 he was awarded the John Fritz
medal for "his contribution to the early development of the
Bessemer process." The J. Edgar Thomson Works which
Carnegie named after the President of the Pennsylvania Railroad, probably to placate him, had the first organized steel
laboratory in this country following Dudley's inaugural work
at Altoona. In those days, almost a week was required for a
complete steel analysis as compared with a few hours today.
This was made possible in a large degree by the discovery of
Wright, when a pupil at the Western University of Pennsylvania, of a method of purifying molybdic acid which enabled
a phosphorus determination to be made in a few hours instead
of days as previously, and to the rapid methods of carbon
determination inaugurated by Charles Morris Johnson at the
Park Steel Works, Pittsburgh, Pa.

ALEXANDER DALLAS BACHE

THE contributions to the advancement of chemistry and laboratory work on the part of our Federal, State and Municipal governments, have not received the recognition they deserve. The first important step forward was in 1843, when the United States Coast Survey came under the direction of Alex. Dallas Bache (1806-1867), a great-grandson of Benjamin Franklin and formerly Professor of Natural Philosophy and Chemistry in the University of Pennsylvania, in Philadelphia. An enthusiastic scientist, Bache originated many new methods and displayed great skill in devising new instruments, and he did much to broaden the growing interest in scientific affairs of the period.

Shortly after its creation by act of Congress, the Department of Agriculture in 1862 established the first Federal lab-

CHARLES MAYER WETHERILL

oratory. It was in a dark subterranean room in the basement
of the United States Patent Office and so small as to provide
no space for the chemist's library. Charles Meyer Wetherill*
(1825-1871), one of the best-educated men of his time, who
commenced his study of chemistry in the laboratory of Booth
and Boyé and extended it in France and Germany, was appointed chemist to the department. He was the first official
in the Government service to hold the title of chemist. Soon
after his appointment at a salary of $1600.00† per annum,
Wetherill was delegated to conduct confidential investigations

* Wetherill, C. M., Smith, E. F., *J. Chem. Ed.* (1929).
† Wetherill was invited at a salary of $5,000 per annum to the office of
Assayer of the United States for California, but declined, preferring to con-
tinue his scientific career.

for President Lincoln. Evidently the President was pleased with his services, for he wrote to the Commissioner of Agriculture, "I know not what the law is as to compensation for the Chief Chemist for the Agricultural Department but I certainly think $2500.00 per year, is, in general principle, a modest compensation for the services of one having Dr. Wetherill's scientific reputation." Wetherill's personality is well described by one of his students, who said of him, "He was one of those Golden Natures who help us form Ideals of Life."

As far back as 1869, following the discovery of oil in Pennsylvania, when little was known about petroleum, the Metropolitan Board of Health of New York encouraged Charles F. Chandler to investigate and to advise them on the dangers of kerosene oil, and the protection of the community against disease which led to Chandler's chemical investigation of the city's water supply. The city fathers were so impressed with Chandler's scientific reports and recommendations that they created for him the office of Chemist to the Board of Health. His pioneer work soon awakened other municipalities to the value of the chemist.

Chemistry has played a most important role in our agricultural prosperity. The work of the pioneers in American agricultural chemical research, led by Samuel W. Johnson (1830-1909) of Yale College and later by Charles A. Goessmann (1827-1910), the noted teacher at Massachusetts Agricultural College, Amherst, whose work and recommendations resulted in the first effective state laws for controlling the purity of fertilizer and feeding stuffs, received great encouragement with the passage of the Morrill Act in 1862. The Act provided an endowment in the form of a grant of lands for the creation of State Agricultural Colleges and it gave scientific education the greatest stimulus it had ever received, foreshadowing the type of institution envisaged almost forty years earlier by Amos Eaton, one of the first Americans to recognize the value of science to the collective prosperity of the country.

Experimental stations had been established in some of the states prior to the Hatch Act of 1887, which provided Federal support for these stations and for the creation of others in those states which did not have a station. The Adams Act of 1906, increasing the Hatch Act grant to each state to $30,000 annually, with conditions making necessary more fundamental research, led to a marked extension of laboratories for agricultural chemical investigations and gave an impetus of a most far-reaching character to all departments of scientific research. The Purnell Act of 1925, increasing the grant under the Adams Act, the Bankhead-Jones Act of 1936 and the recent Agricultural Adjustment Act for the establishment and maintenance of four regional research laboratories, are added proof of our government's recognition of the value of science to our agricultural welfare.

Although several states enacted Pure Food laws and had established laboratories following the passage of such laws in England, the awakening of the American public mind to an appreciation of the importance of science to the needs of everyday life, was the greatest of the many achievements of Harvey Washington Wiley (1844-1930). After obtaining his B.S. degree in 1873 at Harvard, and teaching chemistry at Purdue University, serving also as State Chemist of Indiana, in 1883 he was appointed chemist to the United States Department of Agriculture, Bureau of Chemistry, Washington, D. C. During his twenty-nine years of service, Wiley built an organization from six to more than six hundred employees. His work, especially the enactment in 1906 of the Pure Food and Drug Act, which he sponsored successfully after prolonged opposition, was responsible for the birth and wide development of laboratories for the scientific investigation and

HARVEY WASHINGTON WILEY

manufacturing control of foods, drugs, beverages, etc., as well as the establishment of government laboratories throughout the country to enforce the Act. Of his many accomplishments, no less an authority than C. A. Browne has said that Wiley's technological work did much toward promoting the modern cane sugar industry. A most versatile personality, gifted for leadership and possessing a sparkling wit and quick repartee, Wiley was one of the founders in 1884 of the Association of Official Agricultural Chemists, an organization which has exerted a most potent influence in the development of scientific agriculture and laboratories.

Wiley was a great believer in having the proper apparatus with which to work, and during his earlier work in standardizing and improving the methods of agricultural chemical analysis, he designed many new forms of apparatus. At one of the annual meetings of the Association in Washington, the author, who was exhibiting some new apparatus and had been asked innumerable questions by Wiley about the then new chainomatic balance, inquired, with some trepidation, whether he thought the exhibit detracted from the meeting. In a flash Wiley replied, "Heavens no—it's the best part of the meeting." Among many associates of Wiley to leave the Bureau of Chemistry to achieve fame and to design apparatus suited to the requirements of an advancing science, must be mentioned Gilbert L. Spencer. He was possessed of unusual aptitude for designing apparatus; and many forms of laboratory apparatus used in the sugar industry—sucrose pipettes, calibrating and filtering devices, vacuum drying ovens, etc.—owe their origin or improvement to him.

The work of the Bureau of Chemistry made organized industry increasingly conscious of the value of chemical research and control. The first laboratory to be established in this country representing an organized industry was that of the National Canners Association, Washington, D. C. They started in 1913 their valuable work for the industry, under the leadership of W. D. Bigelow, formerly Assistant Chief of the Bureau of Chemistry under Wiley.

James Curtis Booth of Philadelphia, in 1842, and J. S. Lovering & Co., sugar refiners of Philadelphia, are said to have been the first in America to employ the polariscope in the analysis of sugar and molasses; but not until the Tariff Act of 1883 was the polariscope legally employed in the classification of sugar for duty assessment. This brought about the establishment of many commercial sugar laboratories.

The scientific investigations conducted at the National Bureau of Standards, Washington, D. C. (established by act of Congress March 3, 1901), arising from the increasing use of calibrated glassware and the growing appreciation of the need of greater accuracy, resulted in higher standards in volumetric apparatus. The preliminary work which had been carried out by the old Office of Standard Weights and Measures, now one of the nine divisions of the Bureau, was placed on a scientific basis at the Bureau by N. S. Osborne* and B. H. Veazey. They developed specifications defining the requisite qualifications for volumetric apparatus; similar work with thermometers and hydrometers was conducted by C. W. Waidner and H. C. Dickinson.

* For results of their work, see National Bureau of Standards, Scientific Paper S 92, April 10, 1908.

A MODERN LABORATORY BUILDING

A GROUP OF AMERICAN CHEMISTS AT THE PRIESTLEY CENTENNIAL AT NORTHUMBERLAND, PENNSYLVANIA, AUGUST 1, 1874

THE formation of the American Chemical Society, now the largest scientific organization in the world devoted to a single science, was a powerful stimulus in awakening much isolated scientific talent in America, and in enabling English-speaking chemists to keep abreast of the chemical research of the world. The year 1774 may well be considered the starting point of modern chemistry, for in that year Priestley discovered the gas he called dephlogisticated air, to which Lavoisier gave the name *oxygen*. One hundred years later, the happy thought came to H. Carrington Bolton (1843-1903) of Columbia College, New York, of proposing a centennial of chemistry. On August 1, 1874, at a meeting of the Association for the Advancement of Science, there was formed a subsection of Chemistry in the Association. At the suggestion of Rachael L. Bodley, Women's Medical College of Philadelphia, the meeting appropriately was held at Northumberland, Pennsylvania where Priestley had spent the last years of his life and was buried, and where might be seen the apparatus designed by this great scientist and used in his classic experiments.

The need of a national and purely chemical society was later urged by those who had attended the Northumberland meeting, the gathering there having shown the desire of chemists to meet together, which resulted in the organization in New York on April 6, 1876, of the American Chemical Society with 53 resident members and 80 non-resident members. The remarkable growth of chemistry and the welding influence of the Society through its meetings and journals is indicated by

*Courtesy of the Edgar Fahs
Smith Memorial Collection,
University of Pennsylvania*

JOSEPH PRIESTLEY

a membership of 3300 in 1907, which in the following thirty
years grew to more than 20,000.

The influence of the Society and its help to America in the
World War are well illustrated by a public address of the
Secretary of War,* who said:

> "The American Chemical Society presented a striking in-
> stance of preparedness. It certainly had the largest body of its
> kind in the world and comprised in its ranks 14,500 of the
> 17,000 chemists of the country, and when the country's call
> went out for chemists the co-operation of this Society was a
> splendid substitute for any preparation the Government had
> to make. Almost instantly the Government was able to put

* *J. Ind. Eng. Chem.,* 11, 921-24 (1919).

its hand on the man who was needed for the particular job, to call him to Washington or service wherever he might be needed. Your Society was by its very existence anticipatory of the calling into being of the forces to collect these data, and the Government owes to this Society, therefore, a debt of gratitude for this closeness of association and intimate knowledge of the profession, which it was able to place at the Government's disposal and thereby to render the chemical knowledge of the country speedily available. The chemists did their share. They did it superbly."

In chemistry also, we are now conscious of the continuity of man's intellectual efforts; no longer does the current generation view the work of its forerunners with a disdainful lack of appreciation; and far from claiming infallibility, each successive age recognizes the duty of developing its heritage from the past.

KEKULÉ.

FROM the termination of the Civil War until the turn of the century, our United States grew from an agricultural society, enjoying simple comforts, to a predominantly industrial civilization enjoying greater luxury than the world had ever known, with industry rapidly becoming established on science. During this same period, a constantly increasing number of academic institutions came to offer courses in chemistry with well-equipped laboratories, in many cases under the leadership of scientists who had studied under the great German teachers. By the turn of the century, our educational and laboratory facilities for the study of chemistry had advanced to such a degree that it was no longer necessary for our students to go abroad for their doctorates.

The twentieth century opened with much evidence of our remarkable progress in many divisions of science. This progress was greatly accelerated by the World War, when we came to realize our dependence upon foreign sources for many important necessities and our lack of plant and industry which could be quickly converted to war purposes, the war in its early stages having drawn attention to previously unthought of applications of chemistry to both offensive and defensive modern warfare. The realization of our weakness and the corrective measures that were inaugurated quickly, created a greater appreciation than ever before of the value of chemistry and the service of the chemist. At the close of the war with its stirring events, there came about a tremendous increase in industrial laboratories for control and research work, and a greater demand for skilled chemists. The subsequent great advance and the stupendous results of scientific application to industry which are beyond the scope of this work, we shall leave for others to record.

Chemistry, which continues its onward march and has shown itself to be the basis of our industrial transformation, is now universally recognized as fundamental to the life of the nation. To keep abreast of the times, laboratory control work and research conducted by our institutions and manufacturers are essential to meet the exacting demands of modern industry and life, and, like the sturdy oak, they continue lustily to grow both in size and strength.

How well America has heeded Pasteur's admonition! What a debt the living generation owes the pioneers of chemistry whom we have briefly reviewed, and the many others too numerous to mention, each of whom in his time advanced the knowledge without which the world could not have been built as we know it!

And so, having paid tribute to some of the directing forces and events which created and stimulated interest in chemistry in our country and brought about a growing demand for chemical laboratory apparatus, let us turn to those who have been responsible for the manufacture and development of this apparatus and its distribution up to the time of the World War.

Part II

ANCESTRY and DEVELOPMENT
of
AMERICAN CHEMICAL LABORATORY
APPARATUS

He who brings the romance of America
to young America has not lived in vain.
                    WILLIAM FREDERICK CODY
                         ("Buffalo Bill").

MANY a youthful American laboratory worker, im-
bibed with the tradition of the natural aptitude of his
countrymen for new enterprises, may wonder why it took
so long for this country to become independent of foreign
sources for most laboratory apparatus. We have seen that not
until the latter part of the nineteenth century could there have
been an appreciable demand in America for chemical laboratory apparatus, other than from the educational institutions.
The requirements of industrial laboratories, important as they
gradually became, were not large enough to justify manufacture by American methods, our manufacturers being little
interested in the production of apparatus for which the demand was limited. As many of our leading chemists had studied
abroad, naturally, they were rather prejudiced in favor of the
apparatus used in their training; and for years the notion persisted, with some justification, that apparatus to be worth while
must come from abroad.

Domestic production of apparatus up to the time of the
World War was so limited that it could hardly be classed as
an industry. The manufacture of most laboratory apparatus
requires skilled artisans, and Europe had the competitive advantage of the early development there of so much standard
apparatus which, with their lower wage scale, gave them the
world as a market. Our manufacturers were unable to compete
as long as the volume requirements of the educational institutions could be imported free of duty, thus encouraging the
institutions to select their requirements from foreign catalogs

and to import direct a single large annual order. From this force of habit, many continued the practice over a long period, in some cases not knowing that less expensive or better domestic apparatus had become available.

The early successful developments in the American manufacture of balances and microscopes in particular, restricted as they were by duty-free imports, not only are a reflection of the progress of chemical science in America but typify, as we shall see, the patience and industry the pioneer manufacturers displayed. The World War gave a great impetus to American chemistry and research and to the development and manufacture of laboratory apparatus, especially glassware and porcelain ware; but at the termination of the war, these infant industries faced the threat of a renewal of intensive foreign competition. Our manufacturers, fortunately, were enabled to consolidate their progress and to extend the products of their perseverance and ability by the action of Congress in 1922, abolishing the duty-free privilege which had been long enjoyed by the Educational Institutions, and advancing the tariff rate on those goods requiring greater tariff protection. This decisive action encouraged the manufacturers to spend large sums to achieve economical quantity production, and their success has enabled the modern generation of American chemists to be brought up on domestic apparatus.

In the following chapters are outlined the origin of apparatus in general use in chemical laboratories, and the developments up to the time when the volume of domestic requirements enabled our manufacturers to demonstrate their ability.

A 15TH-CENTURY ALCHEMIST IN HIS LABORATORY
From Norton's Ordinal
This is probably the earliest representation of a balance in a case*

* With acknowledgment to John Read, "Prelude to Chemistry," G. Bell & Son, Ltd., London, 1936.

ANCESTRY AND DEVELOPMENT   75

Balances

IT IS fitting that we start with the balance, as it is generally considered to be the most important instrument in the
chemical laboratory. From the Latin meaning of the word
balance, bi-lanx = two dishes, the earliest form of weighing
device, having only one pan, was not a true balance.* The
one-pan type of scale which developed into the steelyard, was
followed by the two-pan even-beam scale. The origin of the
modern balance, or equal-armed scale, dates back to the early
Egyptians, as is shown in the very beautiful papyrus of Hun-
nafer, superintendent of the cattle of Sati I, 19th Dynasty,
about 1300 B.C., which is known as the "Ritual of the dead."
The soul of the deceased is shown as being weighed down by
a feather placed on the opposite scale pan. Pictures of early
jewelers and alchemists frequently show a hand scale re-
sembling a type still in use for rough weighing.†

Probably the oldest‡ existing balance used in scientific work
is the one in the Musaeum Ashmoleanum at Oxford University, designed and constructed about 1710 by F. Hawksbee
of London, who is regarded as the inventor of the double-
barreled air pump. A hydrostatic balance for determining the
specific gravity of solids and liquids, it is provided with disc-
shaped counterpoises, glass weight and bucket.

* The reader interested in scales of this period should consult A. Barclay,
"Early Technical Balances," "Sands, Clays & Minerals," Vol. III, No. 3,
London, April 1938.
† See colored illustration opposite.
‡ R. T. Gunther, "Historic Instruments for the Advancement of Science,"
Oxford University Press, 1925.

ANCIENT EGYPTIAN EQUAL-ARMED BALANCE

Joseph Black (1728-1799), Scottish chemist, is given credit for the first use of the balance in quantitative chemistry. His balance,* which is preserved in the Royal Scottish Museum, Edinburgh, we would today term a very clumsy form of an apothecary scale. The beam is 16¾ inches long and the scale pans hang by cords from the ends of the beam by S-shaped hooks. It is interesting to consider that this balance, crude as it is, aided the researches of Black, which marked the beginning of quantitative methods and gave rise to striking improvements in balance design.

The next step forward was the more delicate and sensitive French balance, enclosed on three sides, with the beam raised and lowered by a string attached to the ratchet arrangement in the front. Such a balance was used by Lavoisier and prob-

* A. Barclay, "Some Early Balances," Supplement to J. of S. C. I., Oct. 18, 1935.

JOSEPH BLACK'S BALANCE

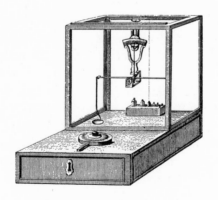

AN 18TH-CENTURY FRENCH BALANCE

BALANCE MADE BY FIDLER FOR THE ROYAL SOCIETY

ably was made for him by Meiguie Le Jeune. In France in
the early days, there were many small shops making balances:
Renaud, in Paris 1806; Fournier, and others; but there is no
evidence that their instruments were used in this country.

The first change to distinguish the ordinary scale from a
precision balance is represented in the instrument introduced
and made in 1789 by Jesse Ramsden (1735-1800) for the Royal
Society, London. Ramsden, of microscope eyepiece fame,
who married the daughter of John Dollond (1706-1761), the
famous English optician, gained great celebrity for his divided
scales, transit instruments, balances and the plate electric
machine which he invented in 1764. The beam of his original
balance is 24 inches long and consists of two hollow brass
cones united at their bases, supported at the center on steel
knife edges turning on agate plates. Sensitive to one one-hun-

dredth part of a grain (½ mg.), the balance was strongly
enough built to support considerable weight. The delicacy of
the fittings, the cones of which must have presented considerable difficulty in construction, is a tribute to the craftsman-
ship of the time. Balances made by Fidler and Troughton of
London were similar in design and construction to the Ramsden type. Silliman, in his Journal,* refers to Troughton, who
he says makes extremely sensible [*sic*] balances. When he inquired the price for one "that would turn with one one-
thousandth part of a grain (0.00007 gram)" Troughton, after
some hesitation replied, "60 guineas." Silliman also says that
instruments were made to order almost exclusively, and that
two years for delivery was not unusual.

It is not known whether Ramsden's balance or the one constructed by Harrison to the design of Henry Cavendish (1731-
1810) was the first to employ knives and planes. The obscurity which hung over Cavendish's private life makes it
impossible to determine in what year his balance was built,
but it is thought to have been used in connection with his
famous researches on the composition of water, completed in
1781. The balance in its case and stand, measures 5 feet 4 inches
overall; the sheet-iron beam is 19½ inches long, and the scale
pans, 4 inches in diameter, have a drop of 20½ inches from
the knife edges from which they are suspended by steel brack-
ets. Cavendish left this balance to his cousin, Lord George
Cavendish, who presented it to Sir Humphry Davy, Bart.
(1778-1829). Eventually it was donated to the Royal Institution, London, where it is on exhibit.

The balance used by John Dalton (1766-1844), propounder
of the atomic theory which marked the beginning of modern
chemistry, now is in possession of the Manchester (England)
Literary and Philosophical Society. This balance, which it is
said was made by Accum,† is similar in size and principle to

* Vol. III, p. 107.   † See page 180.

From an Exhibit in the Science Museum, London

BALANCE USED BY HENRY CAVENDISH

BALANCE BY ROBINSON

an apothecary scale of the time, but capable of arrangement as a hydrostatic balance.

Robinson, a mathematical-instrument maker of London, started to make analytical balances about 1823. He was the first to manufacture on a commercial scale, as well as the first to produce a balance having a triangular perforated beam. His balances, of which there are several in existence, were the first of the precision type to be used in America.

The balance made by Breithaupt of Cassel, for Andrew Ure (1778-1857), of Dictionary fame, presents the last link in design and principle between the early instruments and the modern type. It is not known whether this balance antedates the type introduced in 1846 by L. Oertling, mathematical and philosophical instrument maker of London. Oertling was born in Berlin in 1818, where he served as an apprentice with his brother before going to London. The firm of L. Oertling, Ltd.

From an Exhibit in the Science Museum, London

BALANCE BY BREITHAUPT

whose assay balances in particular were used in America before our manufacturers got under way, still are the leading English makers of analytical balances and weights.

There were several claimants for the credit of having introduced the balance with graduated beam and rider arrangement. The report of the Juries of the International Exposition held in London in 1851, at which most of the important English and Continental makers exhibited, made only one award in this group of the Council Medal, the highest award possible, to L. Oertling, for his balance "with graduated beam and sliding apparatus."

Balances of the Ramsden type were first made in Germany about 1820 by Frederic Apel, the mechanic at the University of Göttingen. From his establishment were graduated many who became famous in scientific apparatus manufacture, including Sartorius, and Gaertner the earliest American manufacturer of spectroscopes. In his youth, Apel proved himself a most skillful mechanic and at Government expense was sent to England, where he acquired a wealth of knowledge. Mayerstein was another early German maker of balances and weights, as was also Staudinger, whose balances were very popular in America before the World War.

The theory that the longer the beam, the greater the sensitiveness of the balance was challenged by Paul Bunge, Hamburg, who in 1866 designed and constructed the first short-beam analytical balance. An engineer especially interested in the design of bridges, which can be visualized from the illustration of the beam of his original balance, Bunge became interested in the subject because of what he thought were mistaken theories held by his friend, a local instrument maker. In the course of years, he developed his theory to an exact and clear form.

After serving his apprenticeship with the renowned instrument maker Apel and working in other precision shops, F. Sartorius of Göttingen, son of the University watch maker, started in business in 1870. He was the first to design and manufacture a short-beam balance using aluminum for the beam. Sartorius had studied chemistry under the famous Wöhler, who placed at his disposal the first aluminum he had produced and taught him how to melt and fuse the metal. Great advantages are claimed for the Sartorius type of balance, which has compensating hangers made in one piece and suspended on three points. For many years before the outbreak of the World War in 1914, the United States imported about forty per cent of the output of the Sartorius factory.

BUNGE'S ORIGINAL SHORT-BEAM BALANCE (1866)

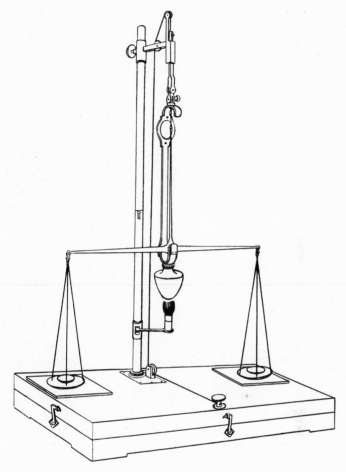

PLATTNER'S ORIGINAL BUTTON BALANCE (1833)

The earliest form of an assay button balance was the scale designed for blowpipe analysis in 1833 by Plattner, Assay Master at the Royal Freiburg Smelting Works and made by A. Lingke, Freiburg (now the firm of Max Hildebrand). The original balance was sensitive to one-tenth milligram when loaded with two decigrams.

Now we turn to the birth and development of American balances. Over the years, all the manufacturers have established a high reputation for the excellence in design and the workmanship of their instruments, so that foreign models now are in very limited use in this country.

BECKER'S ORIGINAL BALANCE
The first analytical balance made in the United States

The pioneer American balance maker was Christopher Becker, who came to New York in 1836 from Arnheim, Holland. An expert maker of astronomical and nautical instruments, he equipped an observatory at 154 Columbia Street, Brooklyn, which was a famous institution in its day. His marked ability was recognized by the local scientific men and

in the early 1850's, Prof. Renwick of Columbia College induced Becker to design and manufacture an analytical* balance. The principle of this balance was a distinct advance in
precision construction and today remains unchanged in the
Becker type balance. The beam arrest is so constructed that
the arms are pivoted about a common axis of the center knife
edge and move through the same arc as the supporting points
of the beam. The success of this balance led Becker to devote
his entire business time to the manufacture of analytical balances and weights, and with his sons, Ernst and Christian, he
established the firm of Becker & Sons. At the outbreak of the
Civil War in 1861, he returned to Europe with his two sons
and established a balance factory in Antwerp, where he was
joined by other sons who had not accompanied their father
to America. After this war, Becker and the sons Ernst and
Christian returned to this country, establishing a factory at
Hudson City, New Jersey, later moving it to Newark and in
1874 to New Rochelle, New York. The other sons of Becker,
whom he had employed in Antwerp, started in Rotterdam to
manufacture balances and weights under the firm name of
Becker's Sons; shortly after, they split up, one brother establishing himself in Brussels under the firm name of H. L.
Becker Fils. Thus it will be seen that the generally held im-
pression that Becker balances are of Dutch origin is unfounded.
Christian and Ernst left their father and in 1884 started their
own business as Becker Brothers, the firm name being changed
to Christian Becker when Ernst died in 1892. The business
continued until 1914, when it was incorporated by the Torsion
Balance Company as Christian Becker, Inc. and the factory
later moved to Jersey City, New Jersey. At his death in 1888,
the business of the father, Christopher Becker, terminated.

* An early Becker balance is exhibited in the Mallinckrodt Chemical
Laboratory of Harvard University. It was found by the author in the base-
ment of the Chemistry Building and reconditioned by courtesy of Christian
Becker, Inc.

Christopher A. Becker, son of Christian, was granted in
1915 a patent for the chainomatic system. This provides the
beam with a special chain attachment by means of which the
use of a rider is obviated and permits weights between 0.01
and 0.0001 gram to be rapidly ascertained. The principle of
the system was conceived and patented in 1890 by Serrin, a
Frenchman, who previously had applied it to electric arc reg-
ulators. The first balance to employ his chain principle was
made about 1900 by Demichel of Paris, who sold his business
in 1903 to Poulenc Frères, later Prolabo Poulenc, the present
French makers of these balances. A similar patent was granted
in 1891 to an Englishman, G. P. Bidder,* Q. C. (1836-1896),
but on the advice of a prominent English scientist, its commercial application was not pursued. The principle was applied
to a scale, however, by the famous Egyptologist, Sir William
M. Flinders Petrie in his work of weighing thousands of
ancient weights.

In Philadelphia, Henry Troemner acted as agent for
Becker & Sons, until he decided in the early 1870's to manufacture analytical balances. A German locksmith, he came to
this country with his friend Meyers and in 1838 started in
Philadelphia to make store metal goods, later engaging in the
manufacture of prescription, jewelers' and grocers' scales and
weights. Troemner probably was the first American to make
scales on the principle of having the load superimposed on,
instead of being suspended from the beam, the invention of
the French mathematician, G. P. Roberval (1602-1675). This
system enabled quicker, if not as accurate weighing although
the Torsion scale which was later developed allowed much
greater precision and accuracy in this type of scale. As far
back as 1856, Troemner started to make for the United States
Mint bullion balances of remarkable sensitiveness considering
their heavy load. One of his earliest analytical balances is il-

* *J. Scientific Instruments*, 1, October 1923.

lustrated in the first edition of "Iron Analysis," by Andrew
H. Blair, the noted chemist who provided America's growing
iron and other industries with analytical methods.

The present firm of William A. Ainsworth & Son, which
remains in family ownership, was founded by William A.
Ainsworth who was born in Lancashire, England, in 1850. His
family settled in Wisconsin and as a youth he worked in the
factory of the Elgin Watch Company. The lure of the West
attracted him in 1875 to Central City, Colorado, and later to
Denver, where he started in business as a jeweler and watch-
maker. Possessed of unusual mechanical ability, Ainsworth
soon mastered the delicate work of repairing assay balances,
usually Oertling's, which the early assayers in Colorado, being
of English birth and education, were accustomed to use and
to send to England for repairs. In 1880 he started to manufacture assay balances and engineering instruments, including the
Brunton pocket surveying instrument so widely used in mining
circles. Later he gave attention to analytical balances, which
in recent years have achieved wide recognition. Ainsworth in
1902 developed a multiweight carrier which eliminates the
use of small fraction weights, up to and including one gram.
He later improved it with a keyboard-operated weight carrier, which tranfers the weight from a special arm to a bar
suspended from the stirrup. This principle, but extended to a
double keyboard-operated weight carrier, which permits the
balance to be checked readily without opening the balance
case, was employed in the balance he built for the National
Bureau of Standards, Washington, D. C., for use in their work
of standardizing analytical weights.

G. P. Keller Mfg. Co., Salt Lake City, Utah, have specialized in what are said to be the finest assay and analytical balances that human skill and ingenuity can produce. German
born, and gifted for tedious work, Keller obtained his experience in the United States, producing his first assay balance in

1896 and analytical balances in 1909. Although over seventy years of age, he continues to do the fine adjustment on all balances made by his firm.

Gottfriend Voland and Henry Van Zelm, who had worked for Becker & Sons, established their business in 1888 at New Rochelle, New York. After Van Zelm's death in 1903, the firm became Voland & Sons, which remains in family ownership and continues to manufacture balances and weights exclusively.

As we have seen, ordinary scales equipped with attachments for determining the specific gravity of solids and liquids, were used in the early days of science. By this method, more accurate determinations were possible than with a hydrometer. The idea of this instrument, re-invented by Robert Boyle (1627-1691) is attributed to the Greek mathematician Archimedes (c. 287-212 B.C.), who established the general principle of hydrostatics. Mohr (1806-1879) introduced a balance designed to indicate directly by means of a rider apparatus the specific gravity of solids or liquids, which was improved by George Westphal of Hannover. His balance, for liquids only, consists of a scale beam graduated into ten equal divisions, fulcrumed upon a bracket which is upheld by a supporting pillar. From the outer end of the beam hangs an accurately adjusted glass plummet weight containing a thermometer, which is immersed in the liquid whose density is to be determined. By means of riders, specific gravity to the fourth decimal place is indicated directly.

It is not our purpose to review other forms of laboratory scales; nevertheless, reference must be made to the Torsion balance, an outstanding American achievement. Experiments were conducted at the University of Göttingen prior to 1880 to utilize a wire for a balance pivot, but without success. It remained for F. A. Roeder at the University of Cincinnati and Alfred Springer in 1882 to perfect the Torsion principle. The meritorious feature of the Torsion balance is that all knife edges and bearings are eliminated; consequently there is no friction. Torsion balances, in many styles to meet the demand of laboratories and various industries, were manufactured by the Springer Torsion Balance Company until 1894, when the business was sold to Fries Brothers of Cincinnati, the present owners of the Torsion Balance Company.

With the great advance of micro-chemistry in recent years, many of our manufacturers offer balances sensitive to 1/1000 mg., and also instruments equipped with magnetic and air damping devices which bring the pointer to rest almost instantly, making possible ultra-rapid weighings.

Agate bearings and knife edges for scales and balances, mortars and pestles, and other agateware, have been made in this country since 1912 by Karl Brächer, Summit, New Jersey. His father operated a small factory in Idar, Germany, where for centuries the industry of agateware was centered because of the abundant local occurrence of agate; today, agate stones from Brazil are mostly used.

the Art of Diſtillation,

A Retort and its Receiver before they be ſet on work.

A Retort with its Receiver, ſet on work.

Oil or Spirit of Salt may alſo be made after this manner.

Take one part of Salt, and three parts of powder of Bricks or
Tiles, and mix them together, and put them into a Retort either of glaſs or earth, to which put fire as before.

After this manner you may make oil or ſpirit of

$$\left\{\begin{array}{l}\text{Nitre}\\ \text{Salt Gem}\\ \text{Alum.}\end{array}\right.$$

Note that theſe Salts muſt firſt be calcined, which is done by
exhaling their flegm.

To

THE ART OF DISTILLATION

By John French, London, 1653
From Edgar F. Smith's, "Old Chemistries."

Chemical Glassware

TO A small band of Phoenician sailors we are said to be indebted for their accidental discovery of glass. According to Holmyard,* the earliest reference to the use of glass for chemical apparatus was made by Zosimos of Panopolis, in Upper Egypt, the most ancient alchemical author, who lived before the end of the third century. Zosimos assures us that the best glass vessels come from Askalon in Syria, an observation also made in the fourteenth century by Cairene.

WOULFE'S APPARATUS FOR THE PREPARATION OF MURIATIC ACID

Chemical glassware of the eighteenth century and earlier comprised mainly retorts, receivers, both plain and provided with tubulures by which connection with other apparatus could be made, alembic heads, bell jars and tumblers. The function of an alembic head was to condense the vapors and to collect the condensed liquor in the fold of the hood. Alembic

* Eric John Holmyard, "Makers of Chemistry," Oxford, Clarendon Press, 1931.

From an Exhibit in the Deutsches Museum, Munich

ALCHEMISTS' GLASSWARE AND APPARATUS

heads consisting of several hoods, one above the other were used in the alchemists' laboratories; and they probably corresponded to the modern fractionating column. One of the first pieces of chemical glassware to become known under what was thought to be the originator's name is the well-known two- and three-necked bottle, said to have been introduced in 1784 by the English chemist, Peter Woulfe (1721-1803). It is thought, however, that the bottle originated with Glauber (1604-1668), the German alchemist, and that it obtained its present name by Woulfe's use of it in his apparatus.

The glasshouse established in Virginia by the Jamestown colonists in 1607 really was the first unofficial American Mint, as long before they made glass bottles, etc., the manufacture of bright glass beads for use in trading with the Indians engaged all their attention. The earliest reference in this country to the manufacture of chemical glassware, seems to be an advertisement in the New York *Gazette* in 1754 of the "New York Glass House Co., dock at North River, near Mr. Peter Mesiers," offering glass bottles, etc., "or any other Chymical Glasses made with all expedition." When the proprietor failed ten years later, it was said "he was deserted by his servants whom he had imported at great expense." This may explain the advertisement of Richard Wisters' Glasshouse, Philadelphia, appearing in the New York *Journal or General Advertiser* of August 17th, 1769:

"Bottles, etc., Receivers and Retorts of various sizes also electrifying Globes and Tubes, etc. As the above mentioned glass is of American Manufactory; it is consequently clear of the Duties the Americans so justly complain of, and at present it seems peculiarly the Interest of America to encourage her own Manufactories more especially those upon which Duties have been imposed, for the sole purpose of raising a Revenue. . . ."

John Donegan and Aloysius Ketterer of Philadelphia made
thermometers and hydrometers as far back as 1785 and advertised "Glasses for Philosophical Experiments." The New
England Glass Company in 1818 advertised in addition to flat
tableware, etc., "Chemical glasses, barometer and thermometer
tubing." They operated until 1887, when due to continuous
strikes and inability to compete with the new Ohio factories
using natural gas, W. L. Libbey, lessee of the plant at that
time, moved to Toledo, Ohio. His plant was the nucleus of
the present Libbey Glass Company. The Union Glass Company at Somerville, Massachusetts, in addition to their main
business of flat tableware, etc., made bell jars, glass tubing,
etc. Labor troubles caused the proprietor, Amory Houghton,
to close down the works. In 1864 he purchased an interest in
the South Ferry Glass Works, Brooklyn, New York, changing the firm name to Brooklyn Flint Glass Works. Houghton
operated the plant until 1868, when he moved the equipment
to Corning, New York, where natural gas was available at the
time, establishing the Corning Flint Glass Works, whose firm
name was changed in 1875 to Corning Glass Works.

There were several other early factories making glass
tubing and druggists' glassware in a small way, including
Hartel and Lancaster Union Glass Works and the Dyottville
Glass Works at Philadelphia; but not until 1873, when a demand for chemical glassware became noticeable, was there an
organized effort in this country to make moulded laboratory
ware and druggists' glassware. The pioneers were Whitall
Tatum & Company, Millville, New Jersey. The glass factory
built in 1806 by James Lee at Millville, which made chiefly
glass bottles, experienced difficulties and passed through many
hands until 1844, when Scattergood, the owner, was joined by
Whitall, a former sea captain. He induced Tatum, a fellow
member of the Society of Friends (Quakers), to join him in
1866, when the firm name was changed to Whitall Tatum &

Company. They first produced in 1876, reagent bottles with moulded chemical names and two years later, a potash glass quite similar to the famous Kavalier Bohemian glass. Their greatest achievement from the laboratory standpoint was the production in 1902 of "Non Sol" glass, the nearest approach until that time to the celebrated Jena glass. The production of this American glassware, limited to flasks and beakers, doubtless would have attained large proportions but for the duty-free importation privilege then enjoyed by educational institutions. It is interesting to note that as late as 1900 it was necessary to place orders by May first for summer requirements, as the glasshouse, because of the heat and making of repairs, was closed down during July and August, a practice no longer necessary because of reserve units and modern ventilation systems. Soon after the close of the World War, Whitall Tatum & Company discontinued the manufacture of most of their chemical glassware utensils, the production no longer being profitable because of factory rearrangement made necessary by machine production of bottles, etc., to which they turned. The Canton Glass Company of Ohio, established in 1882, made some druggists' glassware in addition to their main production. They were succeeded by the Cambridge Glass Company in 1901, who added many moulded laboratory glass items which they still manufacture.

Our limited chemical glassware requirements during the early part of the nineteenth century were supplied mainly by our glasshouses and the few lamp glassblowers who had come to America from England, Italy and France. Glass-stoppered reagent bottles, glass dishes and a few heavy moulded glass articles were imported from France, probably from the Compagnie de Saint Gobain (established in 1665) whose subsidiary, the present "Société Le Pyrex" manufactures "Pyrex" glassware under license of the Corning Glass Works. Other glassware imported from France no doubt came from the firm established by Gay-Lussac (1778-1850), the eminent French chemist and physicist. After his attention had been distracted from purely scientific investigation, he joined in business with the glassblower Collardeau, making chemical glassware, more particularly the burette, alcoholmeter, vapor density apparatus, etc., which Gay-Lussac had originated.

Bohemian potash chemical glassware, chiefly beakers and flasks, manufactured by Francis Kavalier who built his glassworks in 1837 at Sazava, Bohemia, was the early glassware to be imported in quantity into this country. A pioneer in creating a chemical glass industry, Kavalier's start was difficult, as there was neither tradition nor experience in this class of glass manufacture to guide him to meet the requirements of chemistry, which at that time stood on the foundation of its development. The brothers, Joseph and Edward, carried on the work of their father, but in 1857 Edward built his own works at New Sazava. Kavalier hollow glassware, which possessed the qualities of high heat, acid and alkali resistance in greater degree than any other glass, was the world's leading chemical glassware until Jena glass was produced. Before the advent of English fused silica tubing and "Pyrex" glass, Kavalier's hard glass tubing was without equal for combustions.

The systematized development of chemical education and laboratory practice started by Liebig resulted in a flow of new glass apparatus according to the designs of Liebig himself, Hempel, Bunsen, Lunge, Mohr, Fresenius, Geissler and others, enabling Germany to establish a position in the design and manufacture of chemical glassware which was unchallenged until the outbreak of the World War. For a long time, this domination of our trade was aided by the duty-free importation privilege enjoyed by our colleges, the influence of returning American students and our limited requirements not being an incentive to domestic manufacturing.

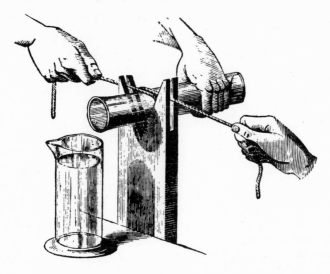

EARLY METHOD OF CUTTING GLASS TUBING
The cord is drawn back and forth until it smokes,
when the glass is plunged into water

As early as the sixteenth century, Venetian and French glassworkers were attracted to the Thuringian forests because of the great quantity of wood available, and the quality of sand which later proved so suitable for chemical ware, as glass made from it did not devitrify when worked before the blow lamp. In the early days, when little was known about the chemistry of glass, F. F. Greiner of Stützerbach, who made toys and glass beads, obtaining his glass tubing from the community glassworks which had been established in Stützerbach in 1808, was the pioneer Thuringian to make lamp-blown chemical ware. He started this manufacture in 1830, and is credited with having done more than anyone to organize the technical education of glassblowers and the system of apprenticeship which aided the district to extend and maintain for so long its lead in this field. Greiner was the first German manufacturer of thermometers having porcelain and paper scales, which art he learned from Berkes, an itinerant glassblower of France, whom he had engaged to make glass eyes and small glass articles. When the firm failed after his death, the glassblowers he had taught scattered, to become the nuclei of the many Thuringian firms specializing in the manufacture of chemical glassware, thermometers and hydrometers.

With the rapidly growing world demand for chemical glassware, many Thuringian factories making general glassware gradually turned to chemical ware. Long before the close of the nineteenth century there had been established many new glassworks, some making both moulded and lamp-blown chemical ware, others mould ware only, and many of them furnishing glass tubing to the numerous glassblowing and graduating shops, both in the towns and nestled alone among the fir-clad hills. Before the birth of the modern organized shop, the home-working industry was quite important; the finished apparatus was taken to the factory on Saturday night and a supply of tubing obtained for the following week's work. This method of work reduced the factory overhead during dull periods of business.

The early Thuringian blow-lamp workers had to contend with difficulties which gradually passed with the introduction of coal gas for heating. Not until 1892 did Stützerbach have a gas plant, when the substitution of gas for wood in heating the glass furnaces made it possible to obtain higher temperatures, and, as a consequence, better quality and easier working glass. "Talg" the fat of the calf, passed through a wick which gave a very sooty flame, was the lamp workers' early fuel and liquid butter* for the finest work. In later years, before coal gas was available to all, which was not until 1904 in some villages, benzine was used; it was contained in a Kipp generator

* Old records indicate that Gundelach often accepted butter in payment of a bill.

and air blown through by means of a foot bellows. Many an American glassblower who has achieved fame in his trade started his career in Thuringia as a foot bellows operator.

Hand Drawing of Glass Tubing and Rod

Of the many notable Thuringian firms in this industry to export their productions to all parts of the world, Emil Gundelach of Gehlberg, whose family started to make glass in 1643 in a shanty in Stützerbach, and Greiner & Friedrichs, also of Stützerbach, were the best known. When Wilhelm Greiner

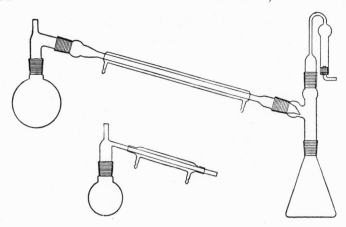

INTERCHANGEABLE GROUND GLASS JOINTS

(not related to the pioneer F. F. Greiner) was joined in 1862 by Ferdinand Friedrichs, who had operated the community glasshouse in Stützerbach since 1839, he had thirty lamp workers. The firm of Greiner & Friedrichs which they founded in 1866 made the first x-ray bulb for Röntgen and they were the first large-scale makers of clinical thermometers.[*] Of their many achievements, the most outstanding is the contribution to the development of interchangeable ground-glass joints. The first step in this revolutionary convenience was taken in the early part of the nineteenth century by the firm of E. Leybold of Cologne, who realized the difficulty of replacing broken parts of the Gaede mercury vacuum pumps which they had introduced. Gundelach extended the idea to a given type and size of apparatus, but it remained for J. Friedrichs in 1926 to recognize the advantage of universal interchangeability and to propose and manufacture a combina-

[*] The invention of Aitken, an Englishman. The first clinical thermometer is said to have been made in the 1870's by L. Casella of London.

Thermometer making is said to have first developed in Italy from whence the tubes were sent to other countries where they were calibrated and finished.

HEINRICH GEISSLER

tion of uniform ground-in connections, independent of the size or type of apparatus. This system has since been adopted by many manufacturers of ground joint glass apparatus.

In addition to the factories and home workers, glassblowers in the German university towns and those attached to the universities became important suppliers of chemical glass apparatus. Outstanding among them was Heinrich Geissler (1814-1870). Educated as a physicist, he settled in Bonn, where he gained a great reputation for his skill and ingenuity in the design and manufacture of chemical and physical apparatus. Geissler is reputed to be the inventor of the tube bearing his name, by which is exhibited the phenomena accom-

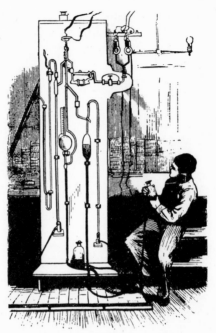

From Frank Leslie's, Jan. 10, 1880

COMBINED SPRENGEL-GEISSLER PUMP AS USED BY EDISON
IN THE INVENTION OF HIS LAMP

panying the discharge of electricity through highly rarefied
vapors and gases, the principle of the modern Neon sign. It
has been said that Julius Plückner (1801-1868) was the inventor of this tube and that for its manufacture "he availed
himself of the ability of the great glassblower Geissler." Edison, in numerous experiments leading to his successful lamp,
experimented with Geissler tubes in an endeavor to increase
their light intensity. Geissler designed and manufactured a
vaporimeter, a mercury air pump which surpassed all previous
forms in simplicity and efficiency, a water suction pump, and

much other apparatus bearing his name, and he modified Mohr's burette by fitting it with a ground glass stopcock. Shortly after his arrival in this country, Ludwig Boehm, one of Geissler's apprentices, was engaged in 1879 by Edison as his glassblower. One of his earliest tasks was to make, according to Edison's ideas, a combination Geissler-Sprengel* mercury vacuum pump. The Geissler pump more quickly obtained a high vacuum than the slower working Sprengel pump, with which a higher vacuum was obtainable. Boehm was hesitant to undertake this difficult task until goaded by Edison, who reminded him that he had not engaged an ordinary glassblower, but a pupil of the great Geissler. The pump was a success, enabling larger quantity production of lamps than had been possible with the Sprengel pump.

Many of the manufacturers constantly improved the quality of their glass, but the most important forward steps to widen the knowledge of the chemistry of glassmaking were the experiments started in Jena by F. O. Schott under the patronage of the State of Prussia. This work resulted in the founding in 1884 of the Jena Glass Works of Schott & Genossen, long famous for their optical glasses, normal thermometer tubings, and laboratory glassware which was in great favor in America until the outbreak of the war in 1914, soon after which it was supplanted by American "Pyrex" ware.

With this background of achievement in the manufacture of chemical glassware and apparatus, it is not surprising that a constant migration of glassblowers came to America from these Thuringian towns and villages. They quickly found employment in our glassblowing shops and the electric lamp factories that sprang up following Edison's epochal invention. In the early days of the electric lamp, expert glassblowers were in great demand for making and keeping in repair the mercury

* Francis Jehl, "Menlo Park Reminiscences," Edison Institute, Dearborn, Michigan.

Courtesy A. Gallenkamp & Co., Ltd., London

MODERN GLASSBLOWING SHOP

pumps used to evacuate the bulbs. The mechanization of the lamp industry fortunately released many glassblowers at a time when they were needed to aid the extension of the domestic chemical glassware industry, when European supplies were shut off because of the World War.

From the glassblowing shops established in New York during the early 1880's by Eimer & Amend and Emil Greiner, came many of our most expert glassblowers and precision calibrators. Greiner, who had worked in the famous Gundelach establishment in Thuringia, achieved in this country a high reputation for the accuracy and precision of his custom-made gas analysis and other graduated apparatus. A great aid to inventors, he personally blew the first model of many devices which became large-scale industries; incandescent lamps for experimenters trying to improve Edison's lamp; radio tubes for de Forest; mercury vapor lamps for Cooper Hewitt; and Thermos vacuum bottles for Walker, who later purchased from Berger of Berlin the American rights to his patent for Dewar vacuum flasks, used as containers for liquid air. Greiner also was one of the pioneer manufacturers of Röntgen's x-ray bulb and Babcock's milk and cream testing bottles. He extended his glassblowing business to the present firm of The Emil Greiner Company, who deal also in general laboratory supplies.

Chemical glassware as an American industry sprang from seeds planted by Whitall Tatum & Company. At their factory in 1880, American-born Evan Ewan Kimble, when twelve years of age, went to work at the unenviable task of firing a wood-burning "glory hole." The knowledge he acquired of glass manufacture caused him to be invited to organize in 1895 a glass vial manufacturing department for the Thomas Shelton Glass Works, at Gas City, Indiana. A few years earlier (1890) S. M. Babcock of the Wisconsin Agricultural Experiment Station had announced his "official test for

Courtesy Corning Glass Works

BLOWING A LABORATORY FLASK IN AN IRON PASTE MOLD

butter fat in milk." This test, which combines the principle of centrifugal force with simple chemical action, revolutionized the dairy industry, as previously the farmer had no means of knowing how many cows in his herd were worth their keep. Within a few years, Babcock's work led to the first real quantity production of graduated glassware in America. Sensing the opportunity, Kimble went to Chicago and with three workers engaged in the manufacture of Babcock's graduated ware for testing milk and cream, and homeopathic vials. The venture met with such success that in 1907 he installed a glass tubing unit at Vineland, New Jersey, consolidating with Victor Durand, a Frenchman, formerly a glass worker with Whitall Tatum & Company who had established a glass tubing factory in 1897.

In 1916, Kimble moved his glassblowing and graduation equipment to Vineland. From a commercial standpoint, the field of volumetric and other laboratory glassware was not considered alluring, but the insistent demands during the early World War days caused Kimble to have his limited crew of lampworkers train all who were willing to learn. At the expiration of the war, with the prospect of an early resumption of importation, continuance of the large demand was uncertain, as American labor costs were very high, and at that time glassblowing depended solely on trained human lungs to supply the power for forming and shaping molten glass. Kimble then made the bold move of acquiring the American rights to the Danner machine for the automatic production of flint glass tubing and rod, and began to spend large sums on the development of improved machines for measuring, dividing and graduating. This resulted in a great extension in the production of calibrated graduated ware, the uniformity of which was greatly facilitated by the machine production of the tubing. The Kimble Glass Company's plant now covers 56 acres and employs about 1500 workers.

VOLUMES ARE ACCURATELY MEASURED AND THE BLANK CYLINDER MARKED WITH
A PASTE-COATED GLASS THREAD

As we have previously mentioned, Amory Houghton, Sr., established the Corning Glass Works in 1875. Signal lights and other railroad glassware, and later on, electric lamp bulbs and electrical insulators were, and still are, their main products. One of their first ventures into the scientific field was in 1896, when Arthur A. Houghton invented the method of drawing thermometer tubing vertically. This revolutionary development contributed to the manufacture of more accurate thermometers, as it forms the tube perfectly, with none of the twisting defects that came from the old horizontal drawing method. Scientists of the Corning Glass Works in 1908, under the direction of Eugene C. Sullivan,* started to engage in chemical and physical research. This research led to such remarkable results as the birth of "Pyrex" brand glass baking ware and in 1916, to laboratory glassware, then mainly beakers, flasks and tubing. "Pyrex" ware has proved an outstanding success, being unequalled in its resistance to heat, mechanical shock and chemical attack and in many respects surpassing the best foreign glass. In recent years, the Corning Glass Works installed lamp-blown departments, so that most forms of glass appartus fabricated from "Pyrex" glass are now available. This outstanding firm has been conspicuous, not only for faith in continuous chemical and physical research work, but for the development of large-scale continuous melting units and automatic machines, enabling them better to cope with the constantly increasing requirements of Industry and Science.

In recent years, many new glassblowing firms have become well established, so that this country is no longer dependent on foreign sources for laboratory glassware.

* In 1929 Sullivan was awarded the Perkin medal for distinguished services to Applied Chemistry.

During the period of the World War, Macbeth Evans Co., Charleroi, Pa.; H. C. Fry Glass Co., Rochester, Pa.; and the Libbey Glass Co., Toledo, Ohio, engaged in the manufacture of beakers and flasks, but after a few years they discontinued the activity.

Courtesy Coors Porcelain Company

CIRCULAR KILN FOR THE BISCUIT FIRING OF CHEMICAL PORCELAIN WARE

Chemical Porcelain Ware

THE limited amount of laboratory porcelain ware used in this country in the early days of science comprised that obtained from Frugier of Limoges, France, and the renowned English pottery of Josiah Wedgwood. To aid the researches of Priestley, Wedgwood, who established his famous pottery in 1759, made and presented to him in 1779 many examples which became the standard forms of chemical laboratory porcelain ware. As other manufacturers came to specialize in this ware, Wedgwood discontinued all but a few types, which his firm still manufactures.

JOSIAH WEDGWOOD
The potter who was infected by Priestley's enthusiasm for chemistry

Before the World War, Royal Berlin porcelain, bearing the blue sceptre trade mark, was world-famous. This so-called "hard paste" porcelain, was known to most laboratory workers because of its extreme resistance to heat and chemical attack. The factory at Charlottenburg, started by the Kingdom of Prussia in 1763 with workmen brought by Frederic the Great from the Meissen porcelain factory, established in 1710, commenced in 1800 to specialize in the manufacture of technical porcelain. In the early days of chemistry in America, Meissen or "Royal Dresden" evaporating dishes and crucibles were preferred, because they were thinner than other types and more suitable for the low-temperature heating devices of the time. Schierholz Thuringian ware, first made in 1817, and Berlin ware with the blue arrow trade mark, made since 1868 by W. Haldenwanger of Spandau, a suburb of Berlin, were long popular in this country for student purposes.

American laboratory workers had little opportunity to suggest new porcelain utensils, as the required types were standardized long before chemistry had made much headway in this country. An outstanding exception is the well-known Gooch crucible for filtering, which F. C. Gooch of Yale University gave to the world in 1878. His method of filtering did not attain wide use until about twenty-five years later, when chemists came to understand better the importance of using the right kind of asbestos.

The pioneer manufacturers of chemical porcelain ware in this country were Pass and Seymour of Syracuse, New York. Richard Pass, a potter from Staffordshire, England, and his son, James, who became an accomplished ceramic technologist, joined the Onondaga Pottery Company, Syracuse, New York in 1875. During the early days of the electric era, when the numerous devices that had been developed frequently proved of uncertain operation, the son James, in 1888, developed a type of electric porcelain which proved most suitable for electrical connections and spark plugs, and later showed its adaptability for chemical usage. Young Pass formed a partnership in 1890 with A. P. Seymour, who at the time was connected with the local electric light company. In 1900 the firm produced porcelain evaporating dishes and crucibles but were forced in 1905 to discontinue the manufacture of this chemical ware, being unable to compete with foreign ware, which at the time could be imported free of duty by the educational institutions, who were then the large users.

"Coors" is the name of the chemical porcelain ware known to most American chemists of today. As a boy in Germany, Adolph Coors worked in a brewery. Shortly after arriving in this country at a time when railroad construction was booming, he went West and became a railroad section hand. With a friend, who also had worked in a brewery, he started in 1872 a small brewery at Golden, Colorado and in 1884, a plant for making beer bottles. The brewery prospered and became famous, but the bottle plant, which later was to give birth to an outstanding new American industry, proved uneconomical and was closed down.

A decorative potter from Bonn, Germany, John Herold, came to this country in 1890, settling in Ohio. A few years later in search of health he was drawn to Golden, Colorado, where large deposits of highly refractory and white burning clays are located. Herold interested the Golden tradespeople, including Coors, in financing in 1908 the Herold China and Pottery Company, to specialize in the manufacture of vitrified cooking ware. For this purpose, the old Coors' beer bottle factory was opened and a kiln built. The venture did not prosper, but Coors took over the business and continued the manufacture of cooking and art ware, later changing the firm name to Coors Porcelain Company.

Following the outbreak of the World War in 1914, Coors received a letter the United States Government had addressed to all domestic potteries, which pointed out the necessity of the development of a domestic chemical porcelain ware. Although little progress had been made with the experiments that Herold had conducted to determine the adaptability of the local clays for chemical porcelain ware, Coors decided to spare no effort or expense to make the United States independent of foreign ware. With this fixed purpose, he had his son Adolph (Cornell, 1907) leave the brewery in 1915 to engage in ceramic research. With a small plant, few employees and scant knowledge of ceramics, young Coors after suffering many disheartening experiences, met with success, producing a ware the quality of which has been constantly improved until it has long since become the equal of the best European product. It is doubtful if America would have become the world's leading producer of chemical porcelain ware but for the zeal and the financial resources of Adolph Coors, Sr. and the patience and marked ability of his son.

During the World War period, chemical ware was imported from Japan, Denmark and England, but importation ceased when the Coors plant came into substantial production. After Herold left Colorado and returned to Ohio, he interested the Ohio Pottery Company, Zanesville, Ohio, and later, the Guernsey Earthenware Company, Cambridge, Ohio, in producing chemical porcelain, but they gave up the enterprise; later, the Champion Company of Toledo manufactured a ware under the trade name of Sillimanite, which they discontinued after a few years.

Fused Silica Ware

FUSED silica ware, a product of the electric furnace is of great value in chemical and research work, as its melting point is much higher than that of glass and it better withstands sudden changes of temperature. Silica tubes made possible the determination of carbon in steel by combustion in oxygen with a rapidity previously impossible. For organic combustions, tubes of clear transparent silica or composite tubes built of both qualities, enable experiments to be carried out safely at temperatures much higher than is possible with hard glass.

Gaudin of Paris in 1839, using Hare's oxy-hydrogen blowpipe, was the first to make fused silica on an experimental scale. Elihu Thompson obtained an American patent in 1902 for making fused silica ware; commercial production was made possible, however, by the process invented by Richard Paget and J. Frank Bottomley, who in 1903 founded the Thermal Syndicate, Wallsend-on-Tyne, England. Their products, which have been a great aid to chemists in analytical and research work, are known under the trade name "Vitreosil." The transparent variety introduced by W. A. Shenstone was developed in England by the Silica Syndicate, who in 1917 combined with the Thermal Syndicate. Transparent ware was also imported from Heraeus of Hanau until 1912, when manufacture was started in this country by the Hanovia Chemical and Manufacturing Company of Newark, New Jersey. The Amersil Company of Hillside, New Jersey, established by W. Trautman, who had been with interests in Germany making silica ware, started in this country to make opaque fused silica in 1914 and transparent ware in 1929.

Filter Paper

T HE word filter, being derived from the medieval Latin
filtrum (felt), it is not surprising that the early operation
of filtering as shown in Libavius' "Alchymia," published in
1606, was the passage of the liquid through a series of conical
felt bags, called by the alchemists "Hippocrates Sleeves." Cotton cloth supported on a wooden frame was later employed,
and toward the close of the eighteenth century, unsized paper
was recommended by Lavoisier as cleaner than cloth or linen.

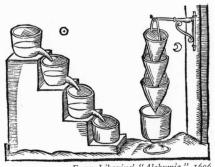

From Libavius' "Alchymia," 1606

FILTRATION BY ROUGH SIEVES

Berzelius, the famous Swedish scientist, is said to have been
the first to suggest absorbent paper of high purity for filtering
purposes. This type of paper, made entirely from rags, which
are essential and are still used for high-grade filter papers, was
first made as a filtering paper about 1810 by J. H. Munktells
at his mill, established in 1740, at Grycksbo, Sweden. When

similar papers for filtering were later produced in England and France, the Swedish paper was catalogued as having "less ashes than other papers." For many years it was the custom of the user to cut circles from sheets, using a template on which would be marked the ash weight of the paper, as determined by the user.

HARE'S
HOT WATER FILTERING
APPARATUS

Early 19th century

In his "Chemical Manipulation" of 1827, Faraday outlines in much detail the importance of selecting a paper shown by the user's personal test to have a low ash content and other desirable qualities for filtering. This may account for the emphasis given the subject by C. U. Shephard, Associate in the Chemical Department in Yale College, in the Appendix to Silliman's "Elements of Chemistry" of 1831. He said, "In order to free filter paper of the lime which it contains (and which comes from the bleaching of the rags by means of chloride of lime) it is generally requisite to digest it in dilute nitric acid and afterwards to wash it thoroughly in warm water—it should be effectively dried afterwards on a sand bath before folding." The limited demand at this time for filter paper for accurate analysis no doubt accounts for the fact that double acid-washed papers, so indispensable for modern rapid methods of analysis, were not introduced until 1883 by Carl Schleicher and Schüll of Düren, Germany, and until 1888 by Munktells, although the difficult and expensive operation of washing paper in hydrochloric and hydrofluoric acids to remove the mineral constituents had been long known. The introduction of acid-washed filter papers was coincident with the period of the first real advance in analytical methods, both here and abroad. The first of the non-acid-washed papers, long familiarly known as "S & S," was offered in 1856; hardened papers for organic work, etc., in 1890; and ether-treated extraction thimbles in 1894. For accurate scientific work, the "S & S" and Munktells papers were the world standards until 1914, when, because of the war, they became available only at infrequent intervals.

James Wardrop, in his essay "Mr. Whatman,* Papermaker" opens with the quotation, "Lorenzo—Beware the departed shade of Mr. Whatman," from Dibden's "Bibliographical Decameron, 11, 338, 1817." He records that James Whatman in England started to make paper in 1740, and that his son, who at eighteen years of age made paper in 1759 and came to be known as the greatest English paper maker of his time, adopted in 1770 the trade and watermark "J Whatman." This has been the mark ever since for the world famous drawing and other hand-made papers known under his name. On Whatman's retirement, the paper mill came under the control of his associate, William Balston, who in 1817 built a new mill. At this mill in 1915, the firm of W. and R. Balston, Ltd. started the manufacture of chemical filter papers, extraction thimbles, etc., which in the ensuing years have gained international fame.

* *Signature*, No. 9, London, July, 1938.

For some years, an imported qualitative paper was acid-washed in this country by the J. T. Baker Chemical Co., and by Baker & Adamson; the former ceased this activity some time ago. Arthur D. Little of Boston, a well-known consulting chemist, in 1917 manufactured an acid-washed filter paper, but the undertaking did not prove a satisfactory venture and was discontinued.

Pierre Prat Dumas, whose predecessors, Prat and Dumas, with long ancestry as paper makers dating as far back as 1470, started about 1840, at Couze, France, the production of filter papers for industrial and scientific use. A marriage resulted in the union of the families as Prat Dumas, a name long famous for filter paper, especially in later years for pharmaceutical purposes. There are several mills in the Couze vicinity operated by relations or connections of this family, manufacturing filter papers of similar quality. With the advance in laboratory technique in this country and with requirements consequently becoming more exacting, the French paper came to be considered too hard for those purposes for which the acid-washed variety was not essential.

Wilson Lysle, who had been granted a patent for his method of crêping the surface of absorbent paper, produced at his small mill at Chesterville, Pennsylvania, in 1889, the first crêped soft filter paper for industrial purposes and general student use. For many years these papers have been marketed by Whitall Tatum & Company. Lysle and the Stevens and Thompson Paper Company, North Hoosick, New York, who made filter paper since 1894 exclusively for Eimer & Amend, were for many years the leading American manufacturers of qualitative and industrial filter papers. Because of the growing demand for their leading productions, Stevens and Thompson discontinued the manufacture of filter paper in 1914, transferring their process to the present firm of Eaton Dikeman Company, who at the time were specialists in the manufacture of blotting and other absorbent papers. The manufacture was transferred to Mount Holly Springs, Pennsylvania, when their Lee, Massachusetts, mill burned down in 1933. H. Reeve Angel & Company, Inc. of New York, introduced in 1917 their now well-known American-made qualitative and industrial filter papers and later, similar papers manufactured in Canada to meet the demands of that country.

Heating Apparatus

A parfet Master ye maie call trowe
which knoweth his Heates high and lowe.
THOMAS NORTON.

THE important role of heating devices in the laboratory, is so well recognized as to require little discussion. Fire was the most important agent of the alchemist, distillation and calcination being the chief operations requiring indirect heating. The means for providing combustion by arrangement of the supply of air under the fire was all-important, but in those days, the principles of combustion were not understood as they are today. Early European text-books abound in lengthy descriptions and precise drawings of the arrangement of the casing and supporting parts of the furnace and the refractory materials that came in contact with the fuel or flame. The design and construction of furnaces changed over the years, as operations became more diverse and wood was supplanted by charcoal, coke, oil, gas and other heating media and more knowledge was gained of the means of assisting combustion to obtain higher temperatures. Before the introduction of coal gas for heating purposes, made possible by Bunsen's invention in 1855 of burning ordinary coal gas with the requisite amount of air to produce a hot smokeless flame, there was designed a wide variety of built-in and portable furnaces for work performed in crucibles or muffles, according to the ideas and particular needs of the designer.

Thomas Fletcher, a dentist of Warrington, England, founder of the renowned firm of Fletcher Russell & Company, Ltd., was one of the first to realize the great importance of

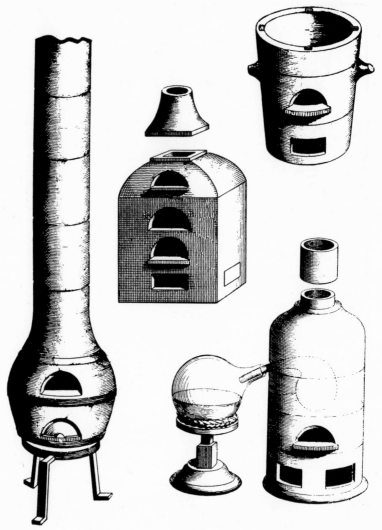

From "Oeuvres de Lavoisier," 1789

FURNACES OF THE 18TH CENTURY

From the Berolzheimer series of Alchemical and Historical Reproductions

DISTILLING OVEN

From Brunswig's "Liber de Arte Distillandi de Compositis," 1500

Bunsen's invention. Fletcher was constantly on the alert for improvements in his professional work and laboratory work generally, and, being a strong believer in the possibilities of coal gas for heating purposes, he started in 1860 to design, and to have made locally, a remarkable range of gas-heated laboratory furnaces, blowpipes, water heaters, burners, foot bellows, etc., which quickly became standard laboratory equipment throughout the world. The appliances met with such favor in this country that the Buffalo Dental Manufacturing Company, established in 1867 by four dentists of Buffalo, New York, made arrangements with Fletcher in 1877 to manufacture in America his entire line of appliances. These devices and their many modifications to meet local and other

Courtesy Journal of Chemical Education

HENRI MOISSAN

conditions found increasing application and popularity until electric heating became the preferred heating medium in laboratories.

A British patent for the first electric furnace was granted in 1878 to Wm. Siemens (1823-1883), born in Hannover, Germany, who after residence in England became a British subject. His work was extended on the scientific side by Henri Moissan (1852-1907), Professor of Chemistry at the Ecole Supérieure de Pharmacie, Paris. He designed and had manufactured about 1880 a carbon resistance furnace giving an intensely hot atmosphere, up to 3500° C., which he used for his work in the artificial preparation of diamonds and other gems, and of many new substances. Moissan furnaces were imported into America and used to a limited extent for research purposes until the advent of the Ajax-Northrop furnace and other American high-temperature furnaces.

Courtesy Eimer and Amend

MOISSAN'S CARBON RESISTANCE ELECTRIC FURNACE

Platinum resistance laboratory furnaces from Hereaus of Germany were imported before the close of the nineteenth century, and Eimer & Amend of New York made small platinum resistance crucible and muffle furnaces, suitable for temperatures up to 1400° C. The American furnaces, having the resistance wire partially exposed, were built in sections so that any part might be readily replaceable in case of a burn-out or accident; this feature was the basis of a patent granted to a New York dentist. This patent was purchased by August Eimer and became the essential principle of the present Multiple Unit furnaces.

Devices heated by the ignition of Thermit, a mixture of iron oxide and finely divided metallic aluminum, discovered by Goldschmidt in 1898, which when ignited, react for about one-half minute generating a temperature up to 2700° C., came into laboratory use for research work requiring very high temperatures, but they did not prove practical.

During the closing years of the last century, several European and American manufacturers offered various forms of electrically heated laboratory apparatus. They constituted an advance, but the short life of the heating-element wire rendered the devices generally unsatisfactory and expensive to maintain. It remained for an American, Albert Leroy Marsh (1877-   ) to make possible the practical and wide application of electric heat for laboratory and household equipment. After graduating in 1901 in Chemical Engineering at the University of Illinois, Marsh started to seek for a durable thermocouple alloy to replace platinum and its alloys, which were then the only reliable materials for this purpose and far too expensive for general use. His research resulted in the now well-known Chromel-Alumel thermocouple alloys; Chromel being a nickel-chromium alloy and Alumel an alloy of nickel and aluminum. Patented in 1905, these alloys were well suited for thermocouple use because of their remarkable resistance to oxidation and their high E. M. F. values. Chromel, the more resistant to oxidation and having high electrical resistance, proved a good heating-element alloy and for that application it was patented in 1906. Shortly after, Marsh began in Chicago the manufacture of a small electric crucible furnace, a tubular type for carbon combustion and a dental furnace for baking enamel on artificial teeth. The eminent Chicago firm of analytical chemists, Mariner and Hoskins, had extended Marsh laboratory facilities for his research investigations, and he honored his friend by naming the firm he organized in 1905 the Hoskins Manufacturing Company. They moved to

ALBERT LEROY MARSH

His resistance wires made possible modern electrically heated
laboratory and household devices

Detroit in 1909 and from their factory has emanated over the
years the widely used electric laboratory appliances known
under their name. Many infringed on Marsh's patents. After
long, expensive litigation he won a great victory in 1915; and
afterward, until the patents expired in 1923, all nickel-chrome
alloy wires used in this country were made by the Hoskins
Manufacturing Company or under their license. Marsh's great
contribution to the electric industry was recognized by the
Franklin Institute, which awarded him in 1936 its John Price
Wetherill medal for his outstanding discoveries.

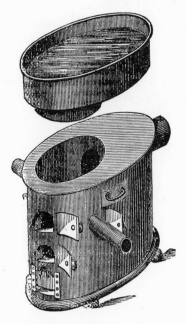

BLACK'S PORTABLE FURNACE WITH SANDBATH

Arranged so that it can also be used for heating the laboratory

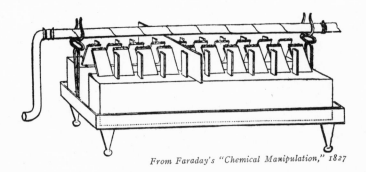

From Faraday's "Chemical Manipulation," 1827

COOPER'S LAMP FURNACE

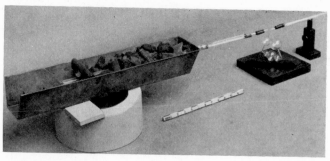

LIEBIG'S CHARCOAL FURNACE AND APPARATUS FOR ORGANIC ANALYSIS (1831)

The Multiple Unit Electric Company of New York, founded by August Eimer, later named the Electric Heating Appliance Company, started in 1911 to manufacture laboratory electric furnaces and hot plates employing the replaceable system of heating units previously mentioned, which enables the user to replace burnt-out parts without having to return the furnace to the factory. These appliances were most successfully re-designed in 1913 by E. L. Smalley, who had been in the employ of the Hoskins Manufacturing Company. August Eimer in 1924 sold his major interest in the company, when the firm name was changed to Hevi Duty Electric Company, and the factory was moved to Milwaukee, Wisconsin. In addition to the well-known Multiple Unit electric laboratory appliances, as the firm name implies, they specialize in the manufacture of large industrial electric furnaces. Not long ago, they built a furnace with normal consumption of 9000 kw. per hour, equivalent to the current consumed in the houses of a city of about 135,000 population.

Early scientific workers had to depend for a long time almost solely on wood-heated furnaces as their heating medium, and on large burning glasses, 12 to 16 inches in diameter as a

From "Oeuvres de Lavoisier," 1789

LAVOISIER'S BURNING GLASS (1774)

source of heat, such as Priestley used in 1774 in his classic experiment by which he discovered oxygen. These glasses were greatly treasured, early scientists often mentioning them in their wills. The use of oil for heating purposes brought about the English invention in 1782 of the Argand circular burner, the parent form of innumerable modifications, including Berzelius' adaptation of it for use with alcohol. Over the years, there was devised a great variety of lamps equipped for use with alcohol, whale and other oils, with and without air blast, and with various arrangements to obtain higher temperatures. In this country, an alcohol blast lamp designed by the noted early American chemist, C. T. Jackson of Boston, was a powerful heating apparatus in its day and was widely employed in laboratories before coal gas was used for heating purposes. Bunsen in 1855, in collaboration with his mechanic Desaga, invented the burner bearing his name, and this type has been used ever since wherever coal gas was available. Chief among the many modifications of the Bunsen burner which have been effected for use with gasoline, natural and other gases, was the Teclu burner invented in 1892, the best burner of its time for purposes requiring a temperature much higher than the Bunsen

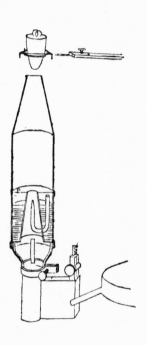

CAMBRIDGE BLAST LAMP

Copied from the lamp used by
E. N. Horsford of Harvard College
when he was at Geissen

burner. It was followed in 1902 by Fletcher's burner, and in 1903 by the French Meker burner. This burner is provided with a meshed grip top which creates a homogeneous mass of burning gas of nearly uniform temperature. In recent years, these high-temperature burners have been supplanted in large degree by the Fisher burner, designed and manufactured by the Fisher Scientific Company, Pittsburgh, Pennsylvania.

From "Scribner's," 1880

EDISON "CARBONIZING" FILAMENTS

A replica of this furnace is in the restored Edison laboratory at
Dearborn, Michigan

The blowpipe is a valuable implement for the chemist and mineralogist to produce a high temperature by complete and rapid combustion. The mouth blowpipe has been in use since the earliest times for urging the fire of small furnaces for goldsmiths' work, etc., but not until about 1758 was it introduced for systematic chemical analysis, by Axel Frederic von Cronstedt, a Swedish Master of Mines. It was later modified by Black, Berzelius, Plattner and others. The flame of wax and tallow candles was first used for blowpiping; later on, lamps were designed to burn different oils, such as rapeseed, olive and whale oils, and a mixture of alcohol and turpentine,

EGYPTIAN WORKER
USING FURNACE
AND MOUTH BLOWPIPE

15th century B.C.

until coal gas, mixed with a sufficient volume of air to oxidize the carbon of the flame, came into general use. Robert Hare of Philadelphia invented in 1813 the oxy-hydrogen blowpipe, first used commercially in the melting of platinum, and Fletcher devised the gas blast blowpipe, many modifications of which have been introduced.

With the advent of electricity as a heating medium, electrically heated laboratory drying ovens with arrangements to maintain a constant temperature were imported from Germany, and the International Instrument Company of Boston made a model. These appliances were not dependable, as the heating wires employed were not easily removable and they

did not have sufficient resistance to oxidation and electric resistance to avoid frequent burn-outs; moreover, the temperature control arrangement, consisting of a magnetic relay,
having mercury as one contact, was unreliable. The first notable advance was the double-walled oven of asbestos wood
having a removable heating element and a sharp and accurate
bi-metallic thermo-regulator with an indicator movable to the
temperature desired, which was designed in 1908 by Thomas
Bruce Freas, then Curator of the Chemical Department of the
University of Chicago, and made by V. Weber, the University mechanician. The commercial manufacture of the oven,
which was extended to embrace models for vacuum, condi-
tioning and industrial purposes, was started by Weber in Chicago in 1909, and later for many years was under the sales
sponsorship of Eimer & Amend, New York. When Freas
joined the faculty of Columbia University, New York, the
business was removed to Newark, New Jersey and operated as
the Thermo-Electric Instrument Company. The firm subsequently was purchased by the Precision Scientific Company,
Chicago, the present manufacturers of the improved Freas
laboratory appliances. In 1924, V. Weber, German-born,
started his own company, the Electric Heat Control Apparatus
Company, Newark, New Jersey, makers of the Weber and
"Elconap" electrically heated and temperature controlled
ovens and water baths. Shortly after the introduction of the
Freas oven, Archilles de Khotinsky, mechanician in the
Physics Department of the University of Chicago, designed an
electrically heated constant-temperature oven and other devices, the commercial manufacture of which was undertaken
and extended by the Central Scientific Company of Chicago.
De Khotinsky, known to his intimates as "Captain," completed
his higher education at the Russian Imperial Naval Academy
in 1869, and during years of service in the Russian Navy, he
advanced to the rank of Captain. His interest in scientific and

technical problems and his acquaintance with Edison, Maxim and other American inventors, caused him to adopt this country as his home. He loved fine mechanical work. His genius and skill in designing were largely responsible for the success of the dividing engine, built under the direction of the noted physicist Michelson* at the University of Chicago, on which were ruled the large gratings that assisted Michelson to win the Nobel prize for his work in determining the speed of light.

* *Cenco News Chats*, December, 1938.

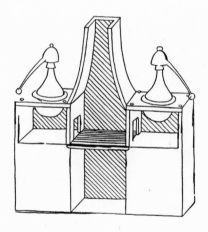

ALCHEMISTS' FURNACE WITH TWO DISTILLATION VESSELS
From a drawing by Leonardo da Vinci about 1500

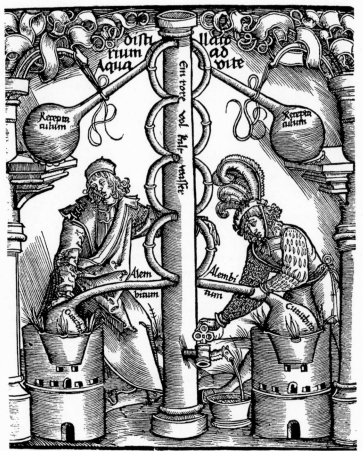

From the Berolzheimer series of Alchemical and Historical Reproductions

A COLUMN STILL BEING USED FOR THE PRODUCTION OF AQUA VITAE (SCHNAPS)

From the title page of volume 2 of the 1507 edition of "Liber de Arte Distillandi de Compositis" of Hieronymus, Brunswig

Metal Laboratory Ware

IN THE early days of Science in America, devices and apparatus of metal which could not readily be made by the experimenter usually were made by a local coppersmith, tinsmith or plumber. As the range of apparatus became extended, several dealers in apparatus established their own shops for the manufacture of metal laboratory ware and wooden ware, importing the newer and more complicated apparatus arising from the rapidly moving European developments in science. The firm of Julius Schober of Berlin, established in 1836, who operates the oldest organized factory in the world devoted to chemical metal apparatus, for many years did a thriving business with our early laboratory apparatus dealers.

URE'S
KETTLE STEAM WATER BATH

From Faraday's
"Chemical Manipulation,"
1827

An expert in metal spinning, a rare art at a time when metal ware was mostly hammered, William Boeckel, who came to this country in 1848 from Goeppingen, Württemberg, founded the company of his name in Philadelphia, Pennsylvania, the pioneer firm in this country to engage in the wholesale manufacture of chemical laboratory hardware and metal ware. At first he manufactured coffee urns, and brass railings so popular in those days. Having made some laboratory metal ware for apparatus dealers in Philadelphia which aroused his interest in chemistry, he decided to engage seriously in the manufacture of this ware. Boeckel found it an uphill struggle to overcome the import habit of the dealers and of the colleges who could import their requirements free of duty; but from a small room, the business grew to occupy in 1923 a modern six-story factory.

The growing demands toward the opening of the twentieth century encouraged several of the dealers in laboratory apparatus to establish their own shops for the manufacture of chemical hardware and their specialties. Louis C. Martens, in charge of the shop of E. H. Sargent & Company, Chicago, started his own business in Chicago in 1908 under the firm name of Humbolt Manufacturing Company. Together with Howard and Morse of Brooklyn, New York, they were the pioneers in this country in the organized manufacture of cement, asphalt and other testing apparatus. The Precision Scientific Company of Chicago, established in 1920 by W. W. Pitann, has become one of our most progressive firms in the field of metal apparatus for laboratory and industrial purposes. Interested in chemistry, Pitann worked for E. H. Sargent & Company during his school vacations, later obtaining a position with them. Seeking a wider opportunity, he affiliated himself in 1919 with the Sargent Steam Meter Company of Chicago, manufacturers of the Sargent gas calorimeter, steam meters, etc. With these appliances as a nucleus, Pitann founded the Precision Scientific Company, with the definite purpose of improving laboratory metal ware. So well has the firm succeeded that they have become leading manufacturers of apparatus for oil, soil, cement and road testing, water stills, electrically heated laboratory devices, burners, etc. In 1935, the firm purchased the concern making the well-known Freas electrically heated ovens, etc.

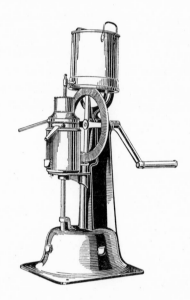

DE LAVAL'S
ORIGINAL HAND SEPARATOR

The application of centrifugal force to the separation of liquids is quite an ancient art. A German brewer seems to have been the first to conceive of its use in the separation of cream from milk, but the practical industrial application of his ideas is credited to Gustav de Laval, a young Swedish engineer of French ancestry. In 1878 he invented the centrifugal cream separator. The original crude machine was the forerunner of the modern centrifuge for scientific and industrial purposes, the manufacture of which has developed into an important American industry. Hand- and water-operated machines with exposed shields containing the glass tubes were first used in the laboratory for the examination of urine and blood, and were extended for use in the testing of milk and oil. Similar machines were later encased in a bowl to make for greater safety in operation; also small perforated basket machines for laboratory sugar testing and other purposes were developed. With the increasing use of electric power, there came rapid developments in centrifugal methods of separation, a great time saver over older methods of gravity settling and suction filtration. Arthur Kendrick (Amherst, 1887), a teacher of physics, who founded in 1903 the International Instrument Company, Cambridge, Massachusetts (now the International Equipment Company), to manufacture physical and electrical apparatus, was the American pioneer in the development of modern laboratory centrifuges. Kendrick designed a fully enclosed and compact motor-driven centrifuge, revolutionary in design and utility, which met with such success that the firm extended the line to embrace machines of several types with a large variety of interchangeable accessories, adapted to a wide range of work. For many years the firm has specialized in laboratory centrifuges and their equipment is used in laboratories throughout the world.

The process of water distillation also is a very ancient one. The Alexandrians used a boiler vessel fitted with a head or cover, called by the Arabians the "alembic." Later on, a side tube was added, which was cooled by passing it through a vessel containing water. Scientific workers in the early decades of the nineteenth century no doubt obtained their distilled water by following the advice Faraday gave in his "Chemical Manipulation" of 1827 :"where steam is used for the conveyance of heat through pipes, the condensed water may by a very little contrivance be collected in abundance, by placing a clean cask or vessel under the place where it issues forth." Then came into use the familiar copper pot boiler with the side tube of the head connected to a block tin-lined worm condenser; later on, steam drying ovens were equipped with arrangements to condense the steam employed for use as distilled water, but these methods did not free the water of dissolved gases. The advance in analytical methods created a greater need for water of high chemical purity; this need prompted Ira H. Jewell, a Chicago engineer, to design in 1900 a bracket type still for gas or steam heating, which automatically and continuously produced distilled water of a greater degree of purity than had been previously obtainable. The F. J. Stokes Machine Company of Philadelphia introduced a variation in design and construction of this still, which has been modified over the years to become a present-day standard apparatus.

ANCIENT STILL WITH
WATER CONDENSER

The pioneer American manufacturers of automatic water stills were Barnstead and Spaulding, of Boston, who started in business in 1878 as manufacturers of plumbing ware. A master plumber of unusual creative and mechanical ability, Barnstead built his first automatic water still in the 1890's for a glass mirror manufacturer who was experiencing trouble because of the impurity of water used in the washing operation. The essential features of his original still are those of the present type; the burner was enclosed to reduce the heat loss to a minimum, and the design permitted the heat generated in the still to be used to preheat the incoming water, and the dissolved gases to pass off. Of the old-fashioned type and lacking business ability, Barnstead did not understand the power and value of advertising, and for many years his still was known only locally. About 1911, its sale was promoted by a laboratory apparatus supply house, when the meritorious features of the still became widely recognized. In collaboration with the General Electric Company, Barnstead introduced the first successful electrically heated automatic water still. The firm was purchased some years ago by interests adopting the title of the Barnstead Still and Sterilizer Company, who have developed a wide range of water stills, etc., for laboratory and industrial use. In recent years several other American manufacturers have developed stills producing distilled water of the highest chemical purity.

At the turn of the century, the improved calorimetric apparatus made available by the Americans, Parr and Emerson in particular, for accurately determining the heating value of solid and liquid fuels, brought about in this country a great interest in calorimetry and the value of fuel testing, which influenced the more intelligent purchase and use of fuel.

The general principles of modern calorimetric methods were started by the eminent French scientist and statesman, Berthelot (1827-1907), the pioneer in using oxygen under pressure to effect combustion. His original calorimeter bomb of 1881 was lined with platinum to withstand the action of the gases resulting from the combustion. It was modified in 1892 by Mahler, who had the instrument maker Golaz of Paris make a bomb with porcelain enamel deposited on the

Courtesy Fisher Scientific Co.

BERTHELOT AND HIS CALORIMETER

The original apparatus is in the museum in the Collège de France

steel, to replace the expensive platinum lining. Modifications of the Berthelot and Mahler calorimeters were made by Fischer, Hempel and others, including Williams of Boston and W. O. Atwater (1844-1907) of Wesleyan University, Middletown, Connecticut. With the introduction of the Parr and Emerson Calorimeters, the imported apparatus became obsolete in this country.

The general principle of the calorimeter designed in 1899 by S. W. Parr of the University of Illinois and manufactured by the Standard Calorimeter Company, Moline, Illinois (now Parr Instrument Company) was similar to that of the early simple Thompson Calorimeter, which used for combustion the oxidizing power of chemicals, enabling determinations to be quickly made with a fair degree of accuracy. Parr later introduced an oxygen bomb calorimeter and after fifteen years of research to eliminate the metallic lining, he produced a new alloy, Illium. This alloy, in addition to its use for his calorimeter bomb, has found valuable application in many fields.

The difficulty of access to the interior of the Mahler bomb made replacement of the porcelain lining a very expensive operation, as the work could be done only in France. This was one of the reasons for the experiments started in 1906 by Charles J. Emerson, when an instructor in the Massachusetts Institute of Technology, to produce a convenient type of oxygen bomb calorimeter of moderate price. His work resulted in the large-scale production in 1908 of an oxygen bomb calorimeter, unique in design and utility, having the essential elements of operation of the original Berthelot type. The bomb, made in two parts, was lined with nickel, gold or platinum, in such manner as to enable the linings to be easily replaceable. In 1926 Emerson further improved his apparatus by using a stainless steel bomb. Parr and Emerson also designed adiabatic instruments which provide conditions where no appreciable amount of heat is lost from, or added to the calorimeter water. This improvement was first developed by Daniells of the Worcester Polytechnic Institute and extended by Flanders, after the suggestions of W. P. Noble.

The first gas calorimeter, introduced by Hugo Junkers of Dessau, Germany, was the standard apparatus in use in this country until modified by C. E. Sargent, a Chicago engineer. He established the Sargent Steam Meter Company, the nucleus of the present-day Precision Scientific Company of Chicago,

Platinum

H E WHO observed, "Nature plays a strange game of hide and seek with mankind, secreting many of the world's most cherished riches with almost fiendish skill" must have had platinum in mind, as the metal is widely distributed, but in very sparse quantities and its refinement constitutes a long and tedious chemical operation. Until 1916, almost 95 per cent of the world production of the metal was from alluvial deposits, but in 1934 it was well below 50 per cent, due to the growing importance of production from primary deposits, such as the arsenide $Pt\ As_2$ Sperrylite, named after F. L. Sperry of Sudbury, Ontario, where occurs the world's chief deposits of nickeliferous sulphide ores. Although the content of platinum metals in these ores is very small, substantial amounts are obtained from the large tonnage of ore treated for recovery of the main products, copper and nickel. The refining of the concentrates is undertaken at the refinery of the Mond Nickel Company at Acton, England. The platinum metal sent to America for fabrication is in sponge form.

The attention of scientific men in Europe was first directed to the metal about 1745, when it was noticed in the gold mines of New Granada (now Colombia) and long regarded as a nuisance. The explorers referred to it as "Platina" a diminutive of the Spanish word "Plata," probably because of the silver-like whiteness of the substance. The first rich deposits of platinum were discovered in the Ural Mountains of Russia in 1822, a few years after the metal had been noticed in the washings from the gold mines. These deposits became the principle source of the world's supply until 1916, when Russia became disorganized and the price of the metal soared, which stimulated production elsewhere, notably in Colombia and

W. H. WOLLASTON

The 1931 Wollaston Medal of the Geological Society of Great Britain. This medal, the centenary award, was struck in palladium presented to the Society by the Mond Nickel Company

South Africa. By 1924, Russia again was the chief producer, with an estimated output of 100,000 ounces, although before the war the production had exceeded 200,000 ounces. In recent years Canada has become the leading world source for platinum, due to the large tonnage of Sudbury ores mined to meet the increased demand for nickel. At the present time the Acton Refinery production of platinum is in excess of 100,000 ounces per annum; it produces also an equal amount of palladium, and lesser quantities of the platinum metals, rhodium, ruthenium and iridium.

Platinum ware occupies an indispensable place in the laboratory for fusions, evaporations, ignitions, etc., and in industry for innumerable purposes. The first platinum crucible appears to have been made in 1779 by the German agricultural chem-

Reproduced by permission of The Worshipful Company of Goldsmiths of London

PLATINUM PARTING APPARATUS, IN REGULAR USE SINCE 1865 AT THE
ASSAY OFFICE, LONDON

ist Achard (1753-1821), who alloyed the metal with arsenic, subsequently expelling the arsenic by heat. The pioneer work of refining and working platinum was undertaken in England by R. Knight, William John Cock, Percival Norton Johnson (grandson of a John Johnson, who is said to have commenced assaying in 1702) and the scientist, W. H. Wollaston (1766-1828). In 1800, Cock originated a wet process of refining platinum, which is generally ascribed to Wollaston with whom he later worked on the discovery of palladium. Wollaston, whose diverse scientific research is shrouded with some obscurity, perfected in 1805 an improved method of making platinum malleable, which he kept secret until just before his death in 1828. Under his supervision, platinum apparatus became readily available, but it is thought that Cock assisted him to develop his process to a successful conclusion and that Johnson commercialized it. The firm of Johnson and Cock, which was founded in 1837, became the renowned firm of Johnson Matthey & Company, Ltd. when George Matthey, noted for his researches to improve the purity of platinum, joined in partnership with Johnson in 1851.

The earliest commercial application of platinum was in France in 1802, when upon the introduction of the metric system, the metal was used for weights. American history records that in 1814 Eric Bollman, a native of Denmark, who was said to have become familiar with Wollaston's secret process of converting grains into bars and sheets, was the first to employ platinum for stills used in the concentration of sulphuric acid; he made a platinum-lined still for John Harrison of Philadelphia. It is recorded in England that in 1839 Johnson constructed a still of 424 ounces weight for acid concentration. In 1814 the Russian government struck medals of platinum to commemorate the occupation of Paris by the Allied armies. Because of the limitation of demand for the metal, Russia instituted platinum coinage in 1828, which was discontinued in 1845 when the market price exceeded that of gold. Specimens of these coins may be seen in the exhibit of Faraday relics in the Science Museum, South Kensington, London.

The French scientist, St. Clair Deville, who had conducted extensive researches on platinum, prepared the metal by a dry method in 1857, using Hare's oxy-hydrogen flame in a small lime furnace. One of the first ingots he made, which he presented to Faraday, is included in the exhibit of Faraday relics previously mentioned. Some years earlier Joaquin Bishop, when collaborating in platinum research with Hare at the University of Pennsylvania, succeeded in using Hare's oxy-hydrogen blowpipe to melt platinum, and his method revolutionized the industry. By this process, platinum was melted with such relative ease as compared with the former difficult and tedious process of consolidating platinum sponge, that Bishop became interested in its commercial development. This led him to es-

Courtesy of Johnson Matthey & Co., Ltd.

FORGING A 400-OUNCE PLATINUM INGOT

tablish in 1842 the first American platinum works, which for a long time made laboratory ware almost exclusively, until platinum began to take an important place in industry. The firm of J. Bishop & Company, Malvern, Pennsylvania, which he founded, is now controlled by Johnson Matthey & Company, Ltd.

In this country, a considerable amount of platinum metals is recovered from scrap, sweepings and the used metal; in 1934 the amount recovered was almost one-fourth of the quantity imported. Until the World War, much of our laboratory platinum ware was imported from France, and commercial ware from the famed firm of W. C. Heraeus, G.m.b.h., of Hanau,

Germany. The platinum purchased for the jewelry business established in 1851 by Heraeus engendered his interest in the application of the metal for scientific purposes, and in the course of years, his firm became the leading German manufacturers of platinum ware. As their agent, Charles Engelhard, born in Hanau 1867, son of a diamond merchant and brother-in-law of Heraeus, came to this country in 1891, at a time when the electric lamp industry was developing a great demand for platinum wire. Acting for a group composed of Johnson Matthey & Company, Ltd., W. C. Heraeus, G.m.b.h., of Hanau, and Desmoutis, Lemaire & Company of Paris, Engelhard acquired in 1901 the business of G. F. Groselmire, Newark, New Jersey, a small manufacturer of platinum wire and sheet, and founded the American Platinum Works. The following year, acting for the same interests, he acquired the firm of Baker & Co., Newark, New Jersey. This firm was started in 1875 by Daniel W. Baker and his sons Charles and Cyrus as manufacturing jewelers, and they gradually developed a small platinum manufacturing business. From these small beginnings, Engelhard, who is now one of the principal partners of W. C. Heraeus, G.m.b.h., has developed the Baker firm to a large enterprise with branches in many countries. With the aid of a staff of research chemists associated with the industrial interests he now controls, which include the Irvington Smelting and Refining Works and the Hanovia Chemical and Manufacturing Company, Engelhard has become the dominant factor in the refining and fabrication of the platinum metals in this country. As a result of the operations of his enterprises and those of the pioneer firm of J. Bishop & Company, together with the action of Congress in 1923, removing platinum utensils from the duty-free classification, this country now manufactures its entire requirements of laboratory and industrial platinum ware and exports to many parts of the world.

Alundum Laboratory Ware

ALUNDUM—electrically fused alumina from the mineral bauxite—a reddish-brown vitreous material, was developed by the Norton Company, Worcester, Massachusetts, primarily for abrasive purposes. Its heat-resisting properties and the growing use of the electric furnace in laboratories urged the introduction of Alundum about 1910 for muffles, tubes, combustion boats, etc.; and later a porous variety for Gooch crucibles, filtering dishes and extraction thimbles was produced. This variety resulted from the accidental discovery by O. P. Amend of the suitability of a type of Alundum for certain laboratory utensils. In the manufacture of Alundum, the crushed grains are mixed with a binding agent of a refractory and ceramic nature, moulded in the manner of a potter, and then burned in a ceramic kiln. Alundum cement is widely employed for coating the inside of crucibles and furnaces for high-temperature work.

Rubber Ware

WHEN we consider that the manufacture of rubber
ware is one of the important key industries of the
world today, it is difficult to realize that a century ago such
indispensable laboratory articles as rubber tubing and rubber
stoppers were not freely available. Rubber was first used solely
as an eraser, no means having been discovered of making it
into solid masses or to facilitate its solution, until 1820, when
Thomas Hancock (1786-1865), in England, perfected his
mastication process, the first notable advance toward the practical utilization of rubber. This process enabled the manufacture of many articles of rubber, including cut sheet from
which tubing was first made. Although Faraday* had indicated
that this tubing was suitable for experiments on gases, it
was apparently unknown in this country, for as late as 1847,
Benjamin Silliman and others described how to make rubber
connections from sheet caoutchouc and how to treat rubber
with ether to obtain it in the form of sheets of any desired
thickness.

The method of putting Hancock's masticated rubber into
solution was advanced by the use of coal-tar naphtha, which
was first employed by Charles Macintosh, a dye manufacturer
of Glasgow, in his process of water-proofing fabrics with rubber solutions, and was patented in 1823. This enabled Thomas
Hancock to help his brother John, who manufactured rubber
ware with materials supplied by Thomas, to extend further
the range of his manufactures. However, so-called "acid-
cured" tubings and moulded rubber stoppers were not possible
until rubber was divested of its adhesiveness, and made to

* *The Quarterly Journal of Science, Literature and the Fine Arts*, p.
364, No. XXXIV, London.

THOMAS HANCOCK

withstand the extremes of heat and cold. The story of rubber
has not been recorded in a sequence of reliably related developments, but it seems that the revolutionary advance was
accomplished by the discovery of vulcanization in 1839 by
the American, Charles Goodyear (1800-1860), which was
patented in 1844, and by the Englishman, Thomas Hancock,
patented in 1843. These processes laid the foundation at about
the same time in this country and in England of the present
mighty rubber manufacturing industry. It would seem that
the phenomenon described as vulcanization is an evolution,

rather than the discovery of an individual. Mr. Brockedon,*
an associate of Hancock, suggested the term "vulcanization"
which owes its derivation to the Vulcan of mythology, as in
some degree representing the employment of sulphur and heat
with which that mythological personage was supposed to be
familiar.

CHARLES GOODYEAR

The firm founded in England by Charles Macintosh manufactured a diverse line of rubber tubings and at about the
same time the manufacture was started in this country by the
Union Rubber Company, Harlem, New York; but for many

* Thomas Hancock, "Personal Narrative," Longman, Brown, Green and
Robert, London, 1857.

years the most suitable tubings for laboratory gas connections were imported, first from France, then from England and Germany. Josiah Tomlinson, brother-in-law of Charles Goodyear, established a small rubber factory at Sandy Hook, Connecticut in 1841. The business did not prosper and was taken over by interests who styled themselves "New York Belting and Packing Company" (now a division of the United States Rubber Company). The successful development of this company is said to have been due to Dennis C. Gately, who prior to becoming their Superintendent in 1856, had spent a year or so with a noted chemist of that period. In the 1870's the firm made the first cloth-impression tubing for Bunsen burner connections, and a little earlier, rubber stoppers. In 1890, several employees of this concern started in Passaic, New Jersey, the Manhattan Rubber Manufacturing Company (now a division of Raybestos-Manhattan, Inc.) whose laboratory rubber wares quickly established a high reputation. For some years, other rubber manufacturing concerns in this country have made a variety of tubings for laboratory work.

The use of cork for closing bottles is said to have been introduced about 1680 by the Benedictine monk, Perignon, which enabled him to invent the wine now known as Champagne. In 1822, Hancock covered ordinary cork with rubber solution, but he left this field of activity to his associate, Brockedon who, having wine corkage in mind, was the first to engage in the manufacture of rubber stoppers and bungs. At first, he formed them of woolen felt coated with rubber solution and then with thin rubber sheet. As this proved too expensive, he used a cotton core, similarly coated, but the color and uneven surface were objected to; moreover, the product would stiffen with cold. The invention of vulcanization enabled Macintosh to manufacture on a commercial scale moulded rubber stoppers as we know them today. They were first made in America in the early 1870's; apparently the quality was not of the best, as the 1872 catalog of a New York apparatus dealer lists both French and American stoppers at $9.00 per pound; with the increase in demand, the domestic product must have improved, as the 1879 catalog of the same dealer lists American stoppers only, at $4.00 per pound.

Optical Apparatus

INTEREST in observational astronomy led to the invention of the telescope, the earliest optical instrument. Its imperfections and Dollond's invention of the achromatic telescope objective in 1757 stimulated much study toward the production of a homogeneous glass for optical purposes, it being realized that the essential properties of glass for such purposes differed widely from those of all other varieties. Notable progress was made over the years and many investigators are entitled to credit for developing and improving optical glass; but it is generally recognized that the investigations of Ernest Abbe (1840-1905) of Jena and of Otto Schott, whose interest in glass was engendered by his father who operated a plate glass factory in Westphalia, brought about the most far-reaching developments in optical glass and technical optical instruments.

In this country, George Macbeth of Charleroi, Pennsylvania in 1888 imported men skilled in making optical glass. The manufacture was successful, but was discontinued because of the competition of lower cost imported glass. The Spencer Lens Company of Buffalo established in 1916 an optical glass plant at Hamburg, New York. It was closed down in 1927, but remains fully equipped to resume manufacture, should occasion arise to make that necessary or advisable. The Bausch & Lomb Optical Company of Rochester, New York who long had realized the need for domestic optical glass, began experimenting in 1912, and by 1917 they produced a glass equal to the best made abroad. When the United States entered the World War in 1917, the plant, which today continues in active operation, was extended to supply the additional needs for military and naval optical instruments.

The development of optical glass made possible new and improved optical instruments for research and general laboratory work. The high degree of scientific precision and skill in workmanship necessary for the manufacture of these instruments was not lacking in this country, but the limited demand before the World War made us dependent on European instruments, except for microscopes, spectroscopes and simple colorimeters, which were manufactured successfully in this country for many years before the war.

JEAN BAPTISTE BIOT

The investigations of the French physicist, J. B. Biot (1774-1862), gave birth to the polariscope, the first optical instrument, after the microscope, to be used in the chemical laboratory. This made possible the polarimetric analysis of sugar. As we have seen earlier, Booth in Philadelphia probably was the first chemist in North America to employ the polariscope in the analysis of sugar and molasses. According to C. A. Browne,

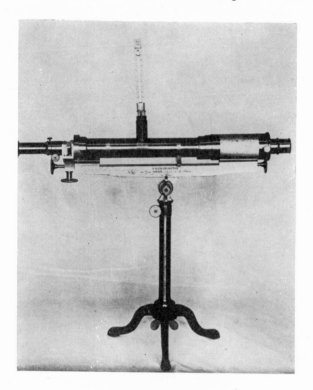

POLARISCOPE USED BY THE LOUISIANA SUGAR PLANTER, VALCOUR AIME

The serial number 64 indicates that it was one of Soleil's earliest instruments

the eminent American sugar technologist, Valcour Aime, a Louisiana sugar planter and refiner, was the first sugar planter in the United States to use the polariscope. The instrument he imported from France about 1850 is exhibited in the Louisiana State Museum, New Orleans, Louisiana.

The essential features of Biot's instrument, which was constructed in 1840, are still retained in modern instruments, although in greatly modified form. The next step in the development of the polariscope was due to the Scotch physicist, William Nicol (1768-1851), whose prism, which he invented in 1828, constitutes the essential feature of all polariscopes, as it greatly facilitates the determination of the plane of polarized light. Nicol's prism was applied to the polariscope in 1842 by Ventzke. To the German chemist Mitscherlich (1794-1863) is due the introduction of monochromatic light into polarimetry. His modification of Biot's instrument was followed by that of Soleil, a French physicist, who introduced in 1845 quartz wedge compensation, which enabled white light to be used in polarimetry as a means of illumination. After working for a time with his father, Soleil's son established his own business which for many years was directed by the nephew, Laurent, until he sold the business in 1892 to the instrument maker Jobin, now the firm of Jobin and Yvon. After his son had left him, Soleil was joined by his son-in-law, Jules Duboscq, who later went with Ph. Pellin, another noted French manufacturer of polariscopes and saccharimeters. In 1854 Duboscq designed and manufactured the well-known colorimeter bearing his name. Jellett (1824-1888) of Trinity College, Dublin, in 1860 introduced the photometric or half-shadow polariscope. The instrument was further developed by Cornu and extended by Laurent in 1877, whose instrument became the standard in France; but its dependence on monochromatic light limited its usefulness.

Although German science had contributed little that was fundamental to the development of the polariscope, the manufacture of the instrument was actively pursued by the Germans. They became the dominant manufacturers, probably because of the demand for instruments in Germany when the Prussian Government about 1860 instituted the taxation of

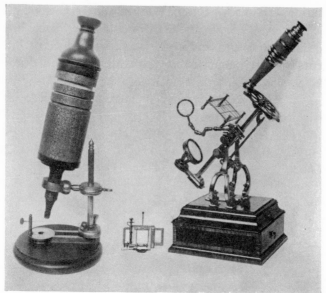

Courtesy The Science Museum, London

A   B

A) HOOKE'S COMPOUND MICROSCOPE DESCRIBED IN HIS "MICROGRAPHIA" (1665), THE FIRST DETAILED AND ILLUSTRATED ACCOUNT OF A COMPOUND MICROSCOPE
B) ADAM'S UNIVERSAL MICROSCOPE, MADE ABOUT 1755. THIS WAS PROBABLY THE FIRST MICROSCOPE TO BE SUPPORTED ON TRUNNIONS

finished sugar. Improvements on the half-shadow polariscope were made by Lippich and Landolt, whose instruments were first manufactured by the present renowned firm of Franz Schmidt and Haensch of Berlin, the constructors of optical instruments for the Reichsanstalt, according to the designs of the celebrated scientists Lummer-Brodhun, Kohlrausch, Helmholtz and others. The firm was established in 1864 to manufacture microscopes, but they gave up this activity after a short time, turning to the design and manufacture of polariscopes, spectroscopes and other optical scientific apparatus. One of their early microscopes is to be seen in the Smithsonian

Institution, Pharmacy Section, Washington, D. C. At the death
of the founders of the firm, their three sons were joined by the
scientists Martens and Szivesey. Josef and Jan Fric of Prague,
constructors of the polariscope according to the design of
Frederick Bates of the National Bureau of Standards, Washington, D. C., also were early manufacturers whose instruments gained world fame.

ERNEST ABBE
The Great German optical scientist

The little workshop which the instrument maker Carl Zeiss
(1816-1888) started in Jena in 1840 with three employees has
grown to a world-famed establishment, occupying an area of
125 acres and producing a wide range of optical scientific

instruments. Prior to the researches of Abbe (1840-1905), who began his connection with Zeiss in 1866, the microscope was the result of rule-of-thumb trials, rather than of scientific achievement. Abbe's researches and those of Otto Schott to improve optical glass, which were conducted under the sponsorship of the Royal Prussian Education office, resulted in the establishment in 1884 of the Jena Glass works, an event which signalized a new era in the development of optical instruments. It is of interest that as far back as 1891, a few years after the death of Zeiss, Abbe surrendered, by deed of gift, ownership of the Zeiss Works in favor of the employees, creating the Carl Zeiss Foundation, which provides welfare institutions for the employees and for profit-sharing on their part. In addition to Zeiss microscopes, Abbe's refractometers, etc., which have long been standard equipment in laboratories throughout the world, microscopes and other optical apparatus by Leitz of Wetzlar, and Reichert of Vienna, and others have achieved international fame.

Observations with the modern microscope, an outgrowth of the glass magnifier or simple microscope of the ancients, often lead the way to the solution of problems which would be difficult or impossible by any other method. Probably no discoveries of science have been more startling than those made by means of this instrument. As we have earlier remarked, the manufacture of microscopes was one of our early instrument achievements. What prompted the interest in this instrument of the American pioneer manufacturer, who obtained the only gold medal awarded for microscope objectives at the 1876 Paris Exposition, is not known. As a boy Charles A. Spencer (1813-1881), whose pioneer work was the nucleus of a present-day great concern, without knowledge of producing lenses or of the making of optical glass, established in 1838 a small experimental shop at Canastota, New York, where he made his first microscope. After experimenting with glass

CHARLES A. SPENCER
The pioneer American microscope maker

mixtures, Spencer made optical glass on a small scale for his
own use. A few years later, under the firm name of Charles
A. Spencer & Sons Company, he commenced to manufacture
microscopes for sale. His first apprentice, Robert B. Tolles, a
youthful spectacle maker of Geneva, New York, who later
produced immersion objectives the excellence of which gained
for him international fame, was taken into partnership, when
the firm name was changed to Spencer & Tolles Optical Company. Tolles left the firm in 1867, going to Boston, where he
established his own business. When Spencer died in 1881, the
firm passed to his son Herbert, who was indebted to his father
in no small degree for his optical knowledge and abilities. He

moved the business to Buffalo in 1891, changing the name of the firm to Herbert R. Spencer & Company, later to Spencer & Smith, and in 1895 to Spencer Lens Company. Since that time the firm has developed in addition to microscopes a wide range of optical scientific instruments.

JOHN J. BAUSCH   HENRY LOMB

From very humble beginnings, the present well-known and extensive establishment of the Bausch and Lomb Optical Company of Rochester, New York, was started by John Jacob Bausch and Henry Lomb. In 1849, when nineteen years of age, Bausch came to this country from Suesson, Württemberg, and in the same year, Lomb came from Burghaun, Hesse-Cassel. At that time, America did not offer much opportunity for young opticians, so they engaged in other activities until 1853, when they started to grind spectacle lenses in Rochester,

New York, at a time when that modern thriving city was scarcely more than a village. For many years the business showed no real sign of prosperity to enable them to carry out their ambitions to expand into a wider field of activity. The son, Edward Bausch, who became interested in microscopes and produced their first instrument in 1872, was inspired to a higher plane in optics by the exhibition of European microscopes at the Centennial Exposition, Philadelphia, 1876, where he met many scientists from Europe. The business, however, did not prosper, and within a few years the resources of the firm were almost exhausted. But with dogged perseverance they triumphed over many difficulties and during the ensuing years, with spectacle lenses and microscopes as their mainstay, they developed a wide range of optical apparatus. The comparatively new science of metallography, which has so greatly aided the iron and steel industries, was introduced in the 1860's by the English scientist, Clifford Sorby of Sheffield. It was extended in this country by Albert Sauveur (1863-1939), a Belgian, for many years Professor of Metallography and Metallurgy at Harvard University. About 1902, Bausch and Lomb began their collaboration with him in the design and manufacture of chemical and metallographic instruments and equipment, now so widely used. Bausch and Lomb entered into arrangements with Carl Zeiss in 1907 for the exchange of development and manufacturing methods, mainly in connection with photographic lenses, military optical apparatus, etc. These arrangements were terminated when the United States entered the World War in 1917. After the War, the firm extended its manufactures to include refractometers, saccharimeters, spectroscopes and other scientific apparatus for research and laboratory work, which previously had been imported almost exclusively.

The world owes much to the great teacher, Robert Wilhelm Bunsen (1811-1899), among whose many achievements was

Courtesy Ralph E. Oesper, University of Cincinnati

ROBERT WILHELM BUNSEN

the introduction about 1859, jointly with G. R. Kirchhoff, of their instrument by means of which spectroscopy was reduced to a practical analytical science. The first manufacturer to offer the spectroscope was P. Desaga, Bunsen's mechanician; later the instruments were imported from the English makers, Browning and Hilger, and from Schmidt & Haensch of Berlin, and others.

The manufacture of spectroscopes in this country was developed in 1896 and successfully extended by Wm. Gaertner, who opened a small shop in Chicago. Born at Merseburg, Germany, in 1864, Gaertner was educated at the Berlin school for instrument makers, serving his apprenticeship with an instrument maker at Halle, later being employed at the famous old scien-

tific instrument establishment of Apel at Göttingen, referred
to earlier. In 1889, Gaertner came to the United States to
become instrument maker for the United States Coast and
Geodetic Survey. To enable him legally to hold this position
and in recognition of his scientific achievements, a special
ruling was made by the Treasury Department waiving the
provisions of the Naturalization Law requiring five years' residence before naturalization. The Franklin Institute awarded
him in 1924 the Howard N. Potts gold medal for "notable
achievements as a maker and designer of scientific apparatus."

Every piece of apparatus hides a romance.
                                        HOLMYARD.

*"Of what use are torches, light, or
spectacles to people who won't see."*

Part III

DISTRIBUTORS
of
CHEMICAL LABORATORY APPARATUS

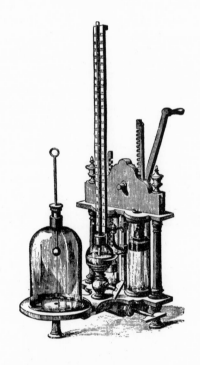

HARE'S AIR PUMP
Early 19th century. Made by Pixii of Paris

T O KEEP pace with the constantly increasing requirements of Science and Industry is the perpetual task of
the modern laboratory apparatus dealer, but little has been
recorded about our apparatus suppliers who have contributed
so much to the convenience of modern laboratory work, and
to the improvement of apparatus. What material assistance
it is to chemists, whether engaged in educational, industrial
or research work, to be able to obtain quickly the requisites for
their laboratory work.

The chemist and laboratory technician of today probably
never gives a thought to the limitation of laboratory materials
available to the pioneer chemists. Working in a modern laboratory, equipped with every required form of apparatus, labor-
saving devices and gadgets and dealer catalogs available listing
every form of apparatus for the pursuits of chemistry and
research, and with the facilities of the telegraph, telephone,
railroad, automobile and air service, it must be difficult for
him to conceive of the difficulties the early chemists had to
meet. What slow progress would be made, if the chemist of
today had to design most of his apparatus and then wait while
it was made or imported.

A century of progress in laboratory apparatus is well illustrated by comparison of the modern dealer's apparatus catalog
with the early pamphlet catalog, such as was issued by Carpenter of Philadelphia in 1833. His catalog lists but a few
pages of what we consider today as most simple apparatus.
In those early days, the demand was limited to the requirements of experimenters for apparatus which they could not
readily make themselves. Opticians and mathematical instrument makers, the pioneer apparatus dealers, made metal and
other apparatus for demonstration purposes, importing most
of the glassware born of the developments in science that
were taking place in Europe. They could not greatly extend

their business, as the colleges, the chief users of apparatus,
early acquired the habit of importing direct, a practice which
many continued over a long period.

The amazing march of chemical progress in this country
brought about a great increase in the demand for chemical
laboratory apparatus. Prior to the World War, with our dependence on Germany for so much general laboratory ware,
the path of the small dealer was difficult. The facility of
domestic supplies following the war, however, gave rise to a
marked growth in the number of local dealers in different
parts of the country. They are too numerous to mention here,
so we must confine the brief historical outline to our early
suppliers and the American dealers from the early days until
the World War.

THE first recorded importation of apparatus and chemicals into North America was made by John Winthrop the Younger (1606-1676) according to the invoice* of March,

JOHN WINTHROP, JR.

1633, of Kirby, a London merchant who collected and shipped supplies for clients in the Colonies. One of our earliest suppliers of apparatus was Frederick Accum of London, born in Bückeburg, near Hannover. In London, he apprenticed himself to the famous Brande's Pharmacy and later became operative

* Massachusetts Historical Society.

assistant to Sir Humphry Davy at the Royal Institution. A man of remarkable versatility and application, Accum made great efforts to popularize chemistry. In addition to dealing in apparatus, he operated a consulting chemical laboratory, which he broadened into a school for private lectures in experimental chemistry. On completing his studies under Accum, Benjamin Silliman, who had been appointed Professor of Chemistry at

FREDERICK ACCUM

Yale College, placed with him in 1802, what was a considerable order for apparatus in those days. Accum designed and improved apparatus for lecture purposes and a number of our present conveniences can be traced to him. He was the author of many scientific and industrial books, including "Treatise on Adulteration of Food," which marked the beginning of the pure food movement.

John J. Griffin, who suggested the form of beaker bearing his name, was another of our early suppliers of apparatus. A pupil at the Anderson Institution, Glasgow, an institution for the instruction of artisans, he became a prolific writer of books on scientific subjects. The wide reading of his books created such a demand for the apparatus described as to cause his brother in 1826 to start an apparatus department of his publishing business. He named it "Griffin's Bazaar," a description fashionable at the time, intended to indicate the great variety of scientific apparatus held in stock by the firm. This department grew so rapidly that it was separated from the publishing business and removed to London, and for many years was conducted by the sons of the founder, under the firm name of John J. Griffin & Sons. "Griffin's Chemical Handicraft," a pioneer descriptive catalog of chemical and philosophical apparatus, described the apparatus and its use in considerable detail. The limited knowledge of the use of apparatus in those days is indicated by the fact that more than a page was devoted, as late as the 1860 edition, to description of the graduation and use of the ordinary Mohr pipette. The apparatus house is now Griffin & Tatlock, Ltd., the publishing house, Charles Griffin & Company, Ltd., both of London.

Information about early French dealers is rather obscure, but we know they sent supplies to this country, as early American dealers offered French glassware and reagent bottles, porcelain ware, etc. It is highly probable that some of our early glass apparatus came from the firm which Gay-Lussac (1778-1850) founded with Collardeau, for the manufacture of the burette, vapor density apparatus and other apparatus he had originated. The priced inventory* of apparatus and chemicals of the Chemical Laboratory of the University of Pennsylvania, amounting to $693.14, prepared by William H.

* The apparatus according to this inventory apparently was the personal property of Keating. It does not include the apparatus of Robert Hare in the Medical Department.

From "Chemical Recreations," by John Griffin,
Sixth Edition, 1826

Intoxicating Power of Nitrous Oxide Gas

In general the effects are *highly pleasurable*. "Exquisite sensation" of pleasure, an irresistible propensity to laughter, a rapid flow of vivid ideas, singular thrilling in the toes, fingers and ears, a strong incitement to muscular motions —are the ordinary feelings produced by it. The celebrated Mr. Wedgwood "had a violent inclination to jump over the chairs and tables, and seemed so light that he thought he was going to fly." What is exceedingly remarkable is that the intoxication thus produced generally renders the person cheerful and high spirited for the remainder of the day.

THIS CURIOUS PRINT IS REPRODUCED FROM "THE BOOK OF TRADES OR CIRCLE OF THE USEFUL ARTS" (4TH ED.), PUBLISHED IN 1837. IT ILLUSTRATES THE ART OF BILLPOSTING! THE HOUSE OF GRIFFIN, ESTABLISHED IN 1826, IS DESCRIBED ON THE POSTER AS GRIFFIN'S BAZAAR

Louis Joseph Gay-Lussac

Keating in 1826 when he left the University, testifies "the prices on all articles are computed as imported from France." This interesting historic document includes a statement of receipt of the equipment in 1828 by Alex. Dallas Bache (1806-1867). Meiguie Le Jeune, an early French instrument maker, licensed by Louis XVI, King of France, made apparatus for Lavoisier (1743-1794) who extolled him for his ability as a mechanician. Although the French scientists made their own apparatus wherever possible with the aid of an assistant who also sold apparatus, there were numerous small shops in France in the early part of the nineteenth century making and dealing in philosophical apparatus. Meulan in 1806 made chemical blown glassware and Deyrolle, whose firm is still in business although now chiefly in physical apparatus, started in 1831 to deal in apparatus for chemistry. Salleron of Paris, noted for his distilling apparatus and ebulliometer for estimating the percentage of alcohol in diluted liquids, was an early manufacturer and dealer in apparatus. In 1882 he sold his business, with exception of the division making the distilling apparatus, to his employee Demichel. As we have earlier seen, Demichel was the pioneer manufacturer of the chain system balance. In 1903 his business was purchased by Poulenc Frères (now Prolabo-Poulenc).

Philadelphia

THE contributions to the advancement of Chemistry and Industry in America by their early scientists gave Philadelphia that lead in the field of science which it held for so long. At the University of Pennsylvania was installed the first Chair of Chemistry in North America; also there was founded in Philadelphia the first College of Pharmacy, and in 1792 the pioneer chemical society of the world. With this background of tradition and accomplishment, it is not surprising that the city was the cradle of the American laboratory apparatus trade.

As far back as 1785 John Denegan, and also Aloysius Ketterer, who made thermometers and hydrometers, advertised "Glasses for Philosophical Experiments," and John McAllister, Sr., who started in business in 1783 as an optician, became a well-known maker of philosophical apparatus.

Daniel B. Smith, a president of the Philadelphia College of Pharmacy, was the first in this country to engage seriously in the business of chemical apparatus and reagents. To his drug store at Sixth and Arch Streets which he opened in 1819 came many young men to obtain instruction in pharmacy. In 1828, the firm became Smith & Hodgson and in 1849 two of their graduates, Bullock and Crenshaw, purchased the business and for many years did a country-wide trade. Not keeping pace with the times, the business declined, and in 1901 was purchased by the present owners, George D. Feidt & Company.

G. W. Carpenter, who started in business as a wholesale druggist, in the early 1830's added chemical and philosophical apparatus, and English and French chemicals. Carpenter served his apprenticeship with Charles, son of Christopher Marshall, one of the original "fighting Quakers,"* of Philadelphia, who

* A derisive name given a body of Quakers who took up arms in the defense of Philadelphia.

BILL OF APPARATUS AND CHEMICALS SOLD
BY DANIEL B. SMITH OF PHILADELPHIA
TO JONATHAN P. CUSHING IN 1822

(After diligent search the author
is unable to identify Cushing.)

it is said was the first druggist with an appreciable knowledge of chemistry to settle in America. In Carpenter's book, "Essays of Some of the Most Important Articles of the Materia Medica," appears one of the earliest lists of "Chemical and Philosophical Apparatus, Utensils and Materials" which he says are "Manufactured by a distinguished artist of this city and furnished at moderate prices at 'Carpenter's Chemical Warehouse.'" As competition increased, Carpenter's interest in apparatus apparently declined, as he was not long known as a supplier of apparatus. In the 1840's, J. P. Duffey of South 8th Street was known for his "delicate" balances and chemical apparatus, but his business did not long survive.

The rise and decline of the business established in 1850 by James W. Queen, of old Quaker stock, who had worked for McAllister, deserves more space than we can devote to it. Queen, who gained a country-wide reputation for his optical products, gathered about himself a remarkable group of mechanicians and workers. In the course of a few years, he established in addition to his main business of spectacles, etc., departments manufacturing and dealing in microscopes, engineering, meteorological, electrical testing and philosophical instruments, also chemical laboratory supplies. There are many opinions for the decline of this remarkable firm which commenced after its re-organization in 1894 as Queen & Company Inc., causing many of the personnel of the firm to leave and to start their own businesses, or to join others: Thomas, Patterson, Howell (Arthur H. Thomas Company), Williams, Brown (Williams Brown & Earle), Leeds (Leeds & Northrup), Wilson (Precision Thermometer & Instrument Company), James G. Biddle, Bailey (Philadelphia Thermometer Company), Miller (Eberbach Son & Company), Landenburg (Denver Fire Clay Company), Pennock and others. What a different story would be related had these builders been enabled to exercise for Queen & Company the abilities they later displayed in the development of their own businesses!

It remained for Arthur H. Thomas (1872-   ) and his associates to regain and to extend Philadelphia's former prestige in the laboratory apparatus field. After attending the Quaker Westtown School near Philadelphia, Thomas obtained a position with Queen & Company in their Department of Physical Apparatus and later in the Microscope Department. Starting his own business in a small way in 1899, to deal in bacteriological and medical laboratory apparatus, he was joined in 1900 by Patterson and Howell, later adding chemical and general laboratory supplies. The firm has constantly grown, to become one of the largest and best-known houses in the trade. Although not engaged in manufacturing, they are entrepreneurs of many well-known types of apparatus. In 1914 Arthur H. Thomas Company published a catalog, revolutionary in its comprehensiveness and detail, which established a model for later dealer catalogs. This progressive house continues under the active management of the founders.

New York

MR. WOODWARD, whom George Chilton wrote of as "An ingenious mechanic at Greenwich," seems to have been the earliest recorded maker of philosophical apparatus in New York. A chemist and a popular lecturer of his day, Chilton assisted Silliman in revising the 1831 edition of his "Elements of Chemistry." He advertised in the New York *Post* of November 11, 1804, "Having procured at heavy expense an extensive apparatus for illustrating the subjects of Natural Philosophy, etc., my course of lectures on these subjects will soon commence at 34 Cedar Street." In addition to lecturing, Chilton offered for sale reagents prepared by himself and apparatus made or collected by Woodward. His son, James R. Chilton (1809-1863) continued the business, but eventually devoted himself exclusively to the practice of commercial chemistry. In his book "Chemical Instructor" issued in 1833, Amos Eaton, the eminent teacher at Rensselaer Institute, Troy, recommended Chilton's and Feuchtwanger's as a source for apparatus and chemicals. Lewis Feuchtwanger, German-born, was an early authority on gems and minerals, but devoted himself principally to his chemical practice and to the manufacture of chemicals and reagents. In writing of him in 1875, Benjamin Silliman, Jr., said, "His establishment has been known for forty years to American chemists for the manufacture and sale of rare chemicals."

Shortly after his arrival from England in 1804, Benjamin Pike (1777-1863) opened an optical shop at 147 Pearl Street. With his sons, Benjamin Jr. (1809-1864) and Daniel (1815-1893), a manufacturing and dealer business in optical and philosophical apparatus was developed. Meyrowitz, Aitchison and many others who became noted American opticians re-

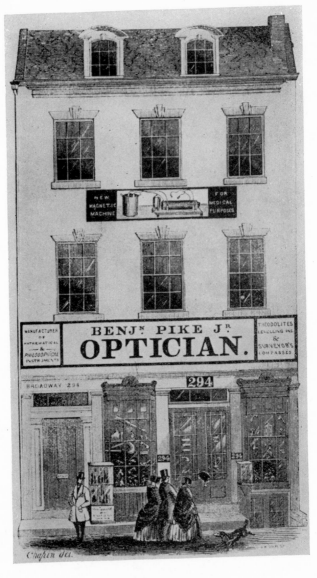

STORE OF BENJAMIN PIKE, JR., AT 294 BROADWAY, NEW YORK

ceived their early training under Pike. Together with his sons he operated under the name of Benjamin Pike & Sons, but the firm came to specialize in optical apparatus when Benjamin Jr. in 1839 established his own business at 166 Broadway. Intensely interested in natural and experimental philosophy and being a mechanic and glassblower of rare ability, he was a great aid to the lecturers of his day. His catalog of 1848, issued in two volumes, which are veritable text-books, describes in detail

FRONTISPIECE
OF PIKE'S 1856
CATALOG

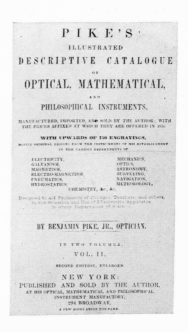

PIKE'S
ILLUSTRATED
DESCRIPTIVE CATALOGUE
OF
OPTICAL, MATHEMATICAL,
AND
PHILOSOPHICAL INSTRUMENTS,
MANUFACTURED, IMPORTED, AND SOLD BY THE AUTHOR, WITH
THE PRICES AFFIXED AT WHICH THEY ARE OFFERED IN 1856

WITH UPWARDS OF 750 ENGRAVINGS,
MOSTLY ORIGINAL DESIGNS FROM THE INSTRUMENTS OF HIS ESTABLISHMENT
IN THE VARIOUS DEPARTMENTS OF

ELECTRICITY,   MECHANICS,
GALVANISM,   OPTICS,
MAGNETISM,   ASTRONOMY,
ELECTRO-MAGNETISM,   SURVEYING,
PNEUMATICS,   NAVIGATION,
HYDROSTATICS,   METEOROLOGY,
CHEMISTRY, &c., &c.

Designed to aid Professors of Colleges, Teachers, and others,
in the Selection and Use of Illustrative Apparatus
in every Department of Science

BY BENJAMIN PIKE, JR., OPTICIAN.

IN TWO VOLUMES.
VOL. II.
SECOND EDITION, ENLARGED

NEW YORK:
PUBLISHED AND SOLD BY THE AUTHOR,
AT HIS OPTICAL, MATHEMATICAL, AND PHILOSOPHICAL
INSTRUMENT MANUFACTORY,
294 BROADWAY,
A FEW DOORS ABOVE THE PARK.

much of the apparatus and their use, and contains upwards of 750 engravings of apparatus for many sciences. In the preface, Pike says of himself that he is not a man of letters, but a mechanic—a practical workman. Despite this opinion of himself, it is manifest from the catalog that he was a clever mathematician and a very practical man of wide scientific knowledge. The American scientific world suffered a great loss by his death in 1864, when the business had to be discontinued.

George Leoni, a mathematical instrument maker at 116 John Street from 1837 to 1846, also was a chemical glassblower. Definite information is lacking, but it seems probable that his business was taken over by Edward W. Kent, a chemist, also at 116 John Street. Kent and his successors, John L. Fyfe and Edward G. Kelley, whose business terminated in 1865, worked at various times in the United States Assay Office. Kent issued in 1848 what was probably the first American catalog (52 pages) devoted to experimental chemical apparatus, rare chemicals and pure reagents. An idea of what the chemist had to contend with in those days is indicated by a lengthy description in this catalog of an apparatus for making water gas for laboratory illumination. In the preface of the catalog, Kent says, "The publication of a work illustrated by so many engravings is necessarily expensive; but contrary to the custom of proprietors of similar establishments in Europe, the subscriber has determined to furnish copies of his catalog gratis, trusting to be recompensed by liberal patronage from the receiver." The present-day apparatus dealer no doubt entertains similar hopes, but hesitates to be so frank.

G. Quettier, a Frenchman, who it is thought was connected with the family in Paris which had made bottles and glassware since 1816, established himself in New York in 1849. Information about his business is not available, but apparently it was quite extensive for those days, as the purchaser, E. B. Benjamin, advertised in 1868 that he had the largest and most diverse stock of scientific apparatus in America. This claim seems justified, judging by his 200-page catalog, the most complete one of the time. Benjamin was of a family which was to become eminent in legal and scientific pursuits. In 1887 he was joined by his son Irving, but in 1892 the business succumbed to competition. Hall, an employee of Benjamin, and Harbeson from Philadelphia established themselves in 1869, a few years later publishing a 200-page catalog. Harbeson sold his interest to J. R. Benjamin, a cousin of E. B. Benjamin, but the business did not long survive. For several years, Hawkins and Wale, mechanicians at Stevens Institute, and other college mechanicians, manufactured and dealt in metal laboratory apparatus, particularly blowpiping apparatus, but importation of the constantly improving European devices presumably caused them to discontinue their business activities. The brothers J. and H. Berge from Hesse established their business in 1850, specializing in assay supplies and Hessian clay crucibles which were very popular in the early days, because of their great resistance to extreme heat and sudden temperature changes. The firm remains in family ownership.

The important Berlin house of J. F. Luhme & Company, operating branches in St. Petersburg and Vienna, who since 1825 had designed and manufactured a great deal of the laboratory apparatus used in continental Europe, established a branch in New York in 1855, and issued an American catalog. The firm in 1865 came under the direction of the partner, W. I. Rohrbeck. The present firm of Franz Schmidt & Haensch of Berlin, long renowned for their polariscopes and other optical scientific apparatus, was a department of Luhme's Berlin house until they started their own business. The New York branch did not prosper and was taken over in 1872 by Rohrbeck's brother and his brother-in-law, Hugo Goebeler. In 1878, the business was purchased by Eimer & Amend.

When Quettier sold his business to Benjamin in 1868 John L. Elmore, an employee, started his own business. He was joined in 1879 by H. E. Richards and later by his brother Leonard Richards, under the firm name of Richards & Company, Ltd. The firm grew in importance and established a Chicago branch in 1890, but due to competition with which they did not have the interest to cope, they sold the Chicago business in 1902 to E. H. Sargent & Company, Chicago, and the New York house to Eimer & Amend. H. E. Richards went into the mining business. Leonard joined his father-in-law in the manufacture of celluloid varnishes at Stamford, Connecticut which business was absorbed eventually by the Atlas Powder Company.

The failure of the late-middle century dealers to realize that experimental chemistry had advanced to a practical science caused members of the old Lyceum of Natural History in 1874, led by C. F. Chandler, to suggest to B. G. Amend of Eimer & Amend, that they add chemical laboratory supplies to their business. At the time, the firm were specialists in imported drugs and chemicals for which they had acquired a national reputation.

Amend, born in Darmstadt in 1821, had studied under the famous Liebig. He came to New York in 1847 at the suggestion of Eben N. Horsford, a student of Liebig's, who in that year was appointed Rumford Professor at Harvard University. Amend came into control of the little pharmacy of W. H. Milner in 1851 and was joined later by his old schoolmate, Carl Eimer. At the time of Chandler's suggestion, Eimer's young nephew August, also from Darmstadt, had been working in the pharmacy since his arrival in New York in 1873. As his father was one of the founders of the Griesheim Chemical Works (now a branch of I. G. Farbenindustrie A. C.) it is not surprising that he had received a thorough education in pharmacy and chemistry. Acting on Chandler's suggestion, Amend sent young Eimer to Germany with ample funds to purchase stocks of apparatus and to establish connections with the leading German manufacturers. This led them to be appointed the sole North American agents for many of these manufacturers, which, together with their understanding of the growing needs of chemistry, soon led to the downfall or decline of many of their competitors. The development of the country-

In the Reconstructed Edison Laboratory at Dearborn, Michigan

Francis Jehl showing Edison how he operated the Sprengel vacuum pump
for Edison's early work with his lamp

wide trade which the firm enjoyed for many years, when local dealers with few exceptions were unknown, was fostered by their Apparatus Manager, John North, a chemical prize winning Englishman from Huddersfield. He inaugurated in 1890 the annual practice of spending many weeks visiting the growing number of educational institutions, experiment stations and industrial chemists throughout the country. In addition to the apparatus business, August Eimer was greatly interested in electrometallurgy. His associates in this field were the original owners of the Willson Aluminum Company, the first commercial producers in America of calcium carbide, the covering patent being sold to interests which later became the powerful Union Carbide & Chemical Company. In these pioneer days when chemistry was beginning to make its influence felt, Edison was a regular visitor to the store of Eimer & Amend and was waited upon by August Eimer, who often went to Edison's laboratory. When Henry Ford decided to erect at Dearborn, Michigan, a reproduction of Edison's Menlo Park (New Jersey) laboratory which was dedicated in 1929, Eimer and Francis Jehl, the only living persons other than Edison himself having intimate knowledge of the old laboratory, were invited to assemble the apparatus, etc., for the restored laboratory. Among many things, this made it necessary for Eimer to visit Europe to have constructed apparatus that long had become obsolete. After inspecting the Dearborn laboratory, Edison, in complimenting Eimer and Jehl, remarked that everything in it reminded him of the stirring days of old, except that it was far too tidy.

The firm of Eimer & Amend may well be called "Fathers of the modern American chemical apparatus business." For many years they have operated glassblowing and instrument shops, besides having sponsored the production of many laboratory devices which are the standards of today. The firm, which remains in family ownership and continues to occupy the original 1851 site at Third Avenue and 18th Street, is under the direction of Carl G. Amend (Columbia 1908), grandson of the founder.

In addition to the dealers mentioned, there were a number of glassblowers, metal workers and college mechanicians offering apparatus, most of whom did not long continue in the supply business. Of the glassblowers, Emil Greiner, whom we have referred to in the chapter devoted to Chemical Glassware, extended his business to embrace chemical laboratory supplies.

Boston

IT IS surprising that in New England, so rich in scientific tradition and whose scientists exercised such an influence on early American chemical education, Boston dealers did not evince much interest in chemical laboratory apparatus until the early part of the present century. For a long time, physical and electrical apparatus primarily engaged their attention, chemical laboratory supplies, except for simple items, being obtained from dealers elsewhere. As we have earlier seen, some chemical ware was made by the New England Glass Company of Cambridge from 1818 until 1887 when the plant was closed down, and the local store of Whitall Tatum & Co. from 1870 onward kept a stock of such chemical and druggist glassware as was made in their New Jersey factory. In the 1860's F. S. Huddleston started to make thermometers and hydrometers, and simple lamp-blown ware was made in the 1880's by J. W. Stanisford & Company at 48 Hanover Street.

The Boston scientific apparatus firms established over the years, many of which experienced troublous times, sprung from the pioneers, Wightman and Chamberlain. Joseph M. Wightman,* born in Boston in 1812 of English parents, was a machinist's apprentice at ten years of age. In 1830, he started in business at 33 Cornhill as a manufacturer of philosophical apparatus. Availing himself of every opportunity to acquire knowledge of natural philosophy and mechanical engineering, he assisted Silliman of Yale during the course of lectures he gave at the Lowell Institute from 1840 to 1842. Wightman was quite active in promoting municipal improvements, and

---

* In the 1850's Wightman acted as local agent for the New York house of J. F. Luhme & Company.

in 1860 was elected as a Democrat, Mayor of Boston. His apparatus business ceased in 1865, when he became the President of the Insulated Telegraph Company.

Nathan Burnett Chamberlain, a machinist at 9 School Street, who in 1832 made apparatus for Harvard College, established himself in 1834 as a manufacturer and dealer of philosophical apparatus. E. C. Ritchie, who was associated with him from 1850 to 1854, started his own business, which was purchased in 1905 by the L. E. Knott Apparatus Company, except for the nautical instrument department which still continues under the Ritchie firm name. Chamberlain was joined in 1859 by his two sons, but the business was discontinued in 1884 when they came to follow other pursuits.

The Franklin Educational Company, established in 1888 by George A. Smith, formerly Purchasing Agent for the City of Boston, had the opportunity to become New England's laboratory supply house. For many years, Smith had traveled abroad to purchase scientific supplies for the Boston schools and had established relations with the leading European suppliers. His firm was the first in Boston to import and to stock a general variety of chemical laboratory supplies, but due to his diverse interests, the business did not long survive.

L. E. Knott, together with Eleazor Cate, founded in 1895 the L. E. Knott Apparatus Company, and as mentioned they purchased the business of E. C. Ritchie in 1905. Knott had been an employee of the Franklin firm, as was Arthur W. Hall, who founded in 1902 the Hall Scientific Company, a reorganization of the Ziegler Electric Company (a merger of Ziegler Bros. and A. P. Gage & Sons) which in 1907 was merged with the Knott Company. Hall joined the Boston branch of the Central Scientific Company of Chicago in 1930 when they purchased the Knott Co. Since then, the chemical apparatus division of this branch has been greatly extended, providing Boston chemists with an improved local service.

Pittsburgh

THE so-called Pittsburgh district, now such a hive of industry and so dependent on laboratory control, did not
early attract an apparatus dealer. Long beyond the days when
the iron and allied industries were forced to adopt chemical
control, local chemists obtained their supplies from New York
and Philadelphia.

The earliest local stock of laboratory apparatus for the
growing iron and steel industry was maintained by the Pittsburgh Testing Laboratory, acting as agents for Eimer &
Amend of New York. Alfred E. Hunt, a graduate chemist
of the Massachusetts Institute of Technology, who became
head of the open-hearth department at the old Black Diamond
Steel Works of Park Brothers, founded in 1883 with George
Hubbard Clapp, a chemist in 1879 at the same works, the
firm of Hunt and Clapp, which they consolidated in 1887
with other consulting interests, under the title of the Pittsburgh Testing Laboratory. In 1888, they sponsored Charles
M. Hall in the manufacture of aluminum by his inexpensive
electrolytic patented process and organized the Pittsburgh
Reduction Company, genesis of the present mighty Aluminum
Company of America. The growth of their consulting and
laboratory work caused them in 1902 to dispose of the laboratory apparatus business to Chester G. Fisher, the twenty-one-
year-old son of a well-to-do oil refiner. He established the
Scientific Materials Company, Clapp acting for a short time
as their first President. Young Fisher, who graduated in 1900
from the Western University of Pennsylvania (now the University of Pittsburgh) was an engineer rather than a chemist,
but he sensed the industrial future of the district and the opportunity it presented. From small beginnings, the firm whose

Courtesy Aluminum Company of America

CHARLES M. HALL

name was later changed to the Fisher Scientific Company, has grown to become one of the most important dealers in this country, with a branch in Montreal, Canada. They are not only dealers, but important manufacturers, as a result of their interest in improvements to existing apparatus and the design and development of new apparatus. The Fisher burner, one of their outstanding achievements, undoubtedly is the most important improvement in burners since the original Bunsen burner. This burner is one of the few laboratory apparatus articles of American design which is exhibited at the Science

Museum, South Kensington, London. The business continues
under the direction of the founder and his sons, Aiken W.
Fisher (Yale 1929) and Benjamin R. Fisher (Yale 1938).

Central New York

FOR many years, the Bausch & Lomb Optical Company
of Rochester, whose birth and development is outlined
in the section devoted to optical instruments, dealt in bacteriological glassware and stains as an adjunct to their microscope business. In 1912 they decided to engage seriously in
the business of general laboratory supplies and established a
lamp-blown chemical glassware factory in Frauenwald, Germany, which was confiscated by the Germans when the United
States entered the World War. By 1919, the laboratory apparatus division had outlived its original purpose and the firm,
desiring to devote all energies to its growing and extensive
optical business, sold this department to W. T. Will, a local
analytical chemist. He established the Will Corporation,
which has flourished under the management of his son.

Ohio

KAUFFMAN LATTIMER COMPANY, wholesale
druggists, Columbus, Ohio, founded in 1881, started
a few years later to deal in laboratory supplies in a small way.
The marked growth of their industrial area and the consequent
advance in laboratory work, both industrial and educational,
decided the firm in 1912 to establish a department devoted to
laboratory supplies. This department has shown continuous
growth.

Chicago

A T FOURTEEN years of age, Ezekial Herbert Sargent (1830-1906), born at Dover, New Hampshire, was apprenticed to the famous pharmacists, Carleton & Hovey, Lowell, Massachusetts. In "covered wagon" days he was induced by F. Scrammon, one of Chicago's pioneer druggists, to join him in 1852. After association with others, Sargent came to own the Scrammon business, but was left penniless by the great fire of 1871. He rehabilitated himself quickly and established a drug-store at Wabash Avenue and 16th Street, in the days when Chicago was the last stop of importance in the West. The growing demand for assay supplies by folk going to the West, induced Sargent in 1878 to add these supplies to his business; later he added general laboratory apparatus. The business prospered, and in 1902 Sargent purchased the business of his local competitor, Richards & Company, Ltd., who in 1890 had established in Chicago a branch of their New York house. At the turn of the century, industrial laboratory demands had grown sufficiently to justify the firm in establishing in 1904 a shop for the repair of balances which had formerly been sent to the makers in the East, and for the manufacture of a general line of chemical hardware. At the death of the founder, the business he had so well established came under the direction of his son-in-law, Thomas P. Smith, Jr., and later under the active management and financial control of F. J. Enright, who had started as an office boy with the firm forty years before.

The firm founded in 1894 by Andrew Daigger, a former employee of Sargent, which he sold in 1916 to Max Woldenburg, formerly a chemistry teacher in the University of Cincinnati, continues under the name of A. Daigger & Company.

The Tools of the Chemist

The National School Furnishing Company, founded in
1871, the cradle of many who started a school supply house
dealing in scientific supplies and of many small manufacturers
of laboratory hardware, was the first Chicago school supply
house to establish a department of scientific supplies. The
establishment of the W. A. Olmsted Scientific Company, one
of the most promising of these early firms, which was under
the management of C. H. Arms, whose son later took an
active part in the Central Scientific Company, was destroyed
by a disastrous fire in 1898 in which Mr. Arms lost his life.
The assets of the Olmsted concern were purchased by the
Chicago Laboratory Supply and Scale Company, who later
were absorbed by the C. H. Stoelting Company. W. M. Welch
Manufacturing Company started in school supplies in 1880
and purchased in 1910 the E. P. Martin Company, when they
started to engage in the laboratory apparatus business.

The Central Scientific Company, organized in 1900 by
Alexander Howard McConnell (1876-1937) and others, purchased the scientific department of the Central School Supply
Company, formerly Alfred L. Robbins Company, who had
taken over a similar department of the National School Furnishing Company. McConnell was joined in 1904 by H. C.
Arms and by Frank Aronson as factory superintendent. Aronson had had long experience in the manufacture of scientific
supplies, having conducted his own shop, where he had manufactured much of the apparatus sold by the many school
supply houses. Later, they were joined by J. M. Roberts and
A. H. Standish. Under able management, the Central Scientific Company, whose trademark "CENCO" is now well-
known, has grown to be a dominant country-wide organization with branches in Boston, New York, Los Angeles and
Toronto, Canada. Paul E. Klopsteg, formerly an Associate
Professor of Physics at the University of Minnesota and later
with the well-known firm of Leeds & Northrup, Philadelphia,

manufacturers of electric measuring and other scientific instruments, is President of this enterprising firm and C. P. McConnell is Chairman of its Board of Directors.

Michigan

CHRISTIAN EBERBACH came to this country in 1837 from Germany, and in 1843 established himself as a druggist at Ann Arbor, Michigan. In 1870, his son Attmar went to Germany for study and on his return the firm, Eberbach Son & Company, started to import laboratory supplies, mainly for educational institutions. While they are well-known dealers in general laboratory supplies, their main interest is the manufacture of laboratory metal ware and instruments, for which they established a shop in 1880. Ralph H. Miller, President of the firm, which is in its fourth generation, was with Queen & Company, Philadelphia, in 1887.

St. Louis

THE limited apparatus needs of the central southwest in the early days were supplied by eastern dealers, until Theodore Kalb (1826-1882) started to import and to supply the requirements of assayers, in particular. He came to St. Louis from Berlin, Germany, in 1847, apprenticing himself to the apothecary, Hückstadt, whose business he took over in 1853. Kalb was one of the founders, and for many years a trustee of, the St. Louis College of Pharmacy. In 1880 he issued what in those days was a most comprehensive catalog of laboratory apparatus and chemicals. At his death in 1882, the business was sold to Henry Heil, who for some time had acted as Kalb's agent in Leadville, Colorado, for the sale of assayers' supplies. Heil (1854-1919), born at Schalkalden,

Germany, came to St. Louis in 1873; while employed as a
drug-store assistant, he attended the St. Louis College of Pharmacy, from which he graduated in 1877. He was a man of
many interests and activities. The business continues under
the name of the Heil Corporation and the direction of Frederick J. Heil, son of the founder.

Colorado

THE development of the vast mineral wealth of the Mountain States naturally led to a demand for assay supplies.
Taking advantage of the opportunity, the Denver drug house
of Bosworth & Hover, established in 1872, started to import
assay supplies in the days when mining was developing so
rapidly that it was a quiet day when they did not sell an assay
balance. The large import of assay clay goods from England
and France led J. O. Bosworth to investigate the fine quality
clays found near Golden, Colorado. With the assistance of
W. E. Burlingame, a local assayer, he developed and perfected
the manufacture of clay crucibles, scorifiers and other refractories, establishing in 1876 the present Denver Fire Clay Company. W. W. Case, a cousin of Bosworth who joined the firm
in 1883, had a creative mind and designed the assay furnaces,
crushers, etc., known under his name. With the growing apparatus demands of industry and the educational institutions, the
laboratory apparatus division of the firm, developed under the
early direction of Landenburger, formerly with Queen & Company, Inc., of Philadelphia, has become the leading apparatus
house in the Mountain States region. Harold O. Bosworth, son
of the founder, is President of the firm, which maintains
branches in Salt Lake City, Utah, and El Paso, Texas.

The Mine & Smelter Supply Company, who deal in supplies
of the nature indicated by the firm name, was established in

1890. They started in 1902 to deal in laboratory supplies, and since then branches have been established in Salt Lake City, Utah, and El Paso, Texas.

Pacific Coast

THE incredible natural wealth of California quite naturally first attracted the miner, prospector and assayer, and led the early dealers in mining supplies to add assay supplies to their business. In these stirring pioneer days, payment invariably was made in gold dust, since coinage was seldom in evidence, and to visit the customer frequently was quite an undertaking, it being necessary to hire a guide and mule pack to get to the mine.

When twenty-two years of age, John Taylor of Westport, Connecticut, who was interested in mining, took passage round the Horn to San Francisco in 1852 and established a business dealing in mining supplies and heavy chemicals. His brother Henry, seeing the need of ore-crushing devices requiring less manual effort than those in use, invented the Taylor Crusher, forerunner of the more highly developed labor saving devices of today.

After completing pharmacy studies at the Chicago College of Pharmacy, F. W. Braun, born at Peru, Illinois, in 1858, opened a drug-store at Roanoke, Texas. With his friend L. N. Brunswig of New Orleans, he went in 1883 to California, and in Los Angeles they established the wholesale drug house of F. W. Braun Company, now known as the Braun Corporation. The growing demands of the mines caused the firm to start an Assay Department, and later to add general laboratory supplies which chemists previously had obtained from the East. Toward the latter part of the century, Braun and his associates became interested in the design and development of assay fur-

naces, burners, crushers and pulverizers for laboratory and
industrial purposes. So well did they succeed that their appliances have gained world-wide renown, as they embrace
outstanding improvements over the former devices. The invention and perfection of their Cary gasoline burner inaugurated the use of gasoline in assay firing furnaces, superseding
the troublesome old coke furnaces used up to that time, especially in remote places where coal gas was not available. These
successes led Braun in 1902 to purchase the Taylor business in
San Francisco, and later to dispose of his drug interests to
L. N. Brunswig. The great San Francisco conflagration of
April 18, 1906, destroyed their local establishment. It was
re-organized in 1908, under the name Braun-Knecht-Heimann
Company who have become the leading Pacific Coast house
dealing in laboratory apparatus.

Justinian Caire, a Frenchman of Briacon, Hautes Alpes,
learning of the opportunities in California for enterprising
young men, went to San Francisco in 1851 and started in the
hardware business. In 1874 he added assay supplies, and laboratory apparatus a few years later. Until recent years his firm
was a prominent Pacific Coast apparatus house.

The Calkins Company of Los Angeles, established in 1898
by Albert C. Calkins to manufacture zinc shavings used in
the gold cyanide process, added furnaces and other assay supplies to the business. In 1902, the firm started to deal in general
laboratory supplies which has become an important part of
their business.

As a result of the Alaska gold rush in 1898, Stewart &
Holmes Drug Company, Seattle (now a unit of McKesson
& Robbins) established a department of assay supplies, which
grew to include general laboratory apparatus. This department was sold in 1924 to the Scientific Supplies Company, who
are now affiliated with the Braun-Knecht-Heimann Company
of San Francisco.

INDEX

INDEX

Burlingame, W. E., 204
Burners, 132, 133, 206
  Bunsen, 132
  Cary, 206
  Fisher, 133, 199

C

Caire, Justinian, 206
Cairene, 93
Caldwell, 39
Calkins Company, 206
Calcium Carbide, first United
  States producers of, 194
Calorimeters, 144
Cambria Iron Works, 53
Cambridge High School, 45
  Glass Works, 97
Canton Glass Company, 97
Carbon determination, rapid
  methods of, 54
Carleton and Hovey, 201
Carlsberg Brewery, 44
  Foundation, 44
  Laboratorium, 44
Carnegie, Andrew, 53
Carpenter, G. W., 173, 183
  chemical warehouse, 182,
  185
Case, W. W., 204
Cate, Eleazor, 197
Cavendish, Henry, 32
  balance, 79
  Lord George, 79
Cement testing apparatus, 140
Central School Supply Com-
  pany, 202

Central Scientific Company,
  136, 197, 202
Centrifuges, 141, 142
Chainomatic balance, 88
Chamberlain, Nathan Burnett,
  196
Champion Company, 116
Chandler, Charles Frederick, 39,
  50, 52, 57, 192
  Museum, 51
"Chemical instructor," 29, 187
Chemistry, pneumatic, 25
Chemists' Club, 51
Chicago College of Pharmacy,
  205
  Laboratory Supply and
  Scale Company, 202
Chilton, George, 187
  James R., 187
Civil War, 87
  effects on chemical educa-
  tion, 52, 66
Clapp, George Hubbard, 198
Clinical thermometer, 102
Cock, William John, 149
Collardeau, 98, 177
College of New Jersey, 20
Colorimeters, 160
  Duboscq, 162
Columbia University, 21, 63, 87,
  136
  School of Mines, 50
  Columbia Jester, 51
Condenser, Liebig, 38
  Mohr, 41
Cooke, Josiah Parsons, 29, 45
Cooper, Peter, 54
Cooper Hewitt, 107
Coors Porcelain, 115
  Adolph, 116

H

$30^{\underline{00}}$